D0544913

GCSE Single Science Workbook

This Workbook has been designed to accompany
our GCSE Revision Guide. It'll test you on everything
you need to know for GCSE Single Science.

It's also got the odd daft bit in to try and make the whole
thing at least vaguely entertaining for you.

H This book is suitable for both Higher and Foundation Tier candidates. The material which
is required only for Higher Tier is clearly indicated with a little H in the margin like this.

What CGP is all about

Our sole aim here at CGP is to produce the highest quality
books — carefully written, immaculately presented and
dangerously close to being funny.

Then we work our socks off to get them out to you — at the
cheapest possible prices.

Contents

Published by Coordination Group Publications Ltd.

Contributors:
Jane Cartwright
Chris Christofi
Charley Darbishire
Bill Dolling
Paddy Gannon
Carol Graves
Sharon Keeley
Alex Kizildas
Simon Little
Tim Major
Glenn Rogers
Dr Nigel Saunders
Rachel Selway
Claire Thompson

ISBN: 1 84146 216 0

Groovy website: www.cgpbooks.co.uk

Illustrations by: Sandy Gardner, Ashley Tyson and Lex Ward
Jolly bits of clipart from CorelDRAW
With thanks to Charley Darbishire, Tim Major, Glenn Rogers and Bob White for the proofreading

Printed by Elanders Hindson, Newcastle upon Tyne.

Cells, Tissues and Organ Systems

Q1   The following diagram shows a simple animal cell.
Name the parts labelled A, B and C.

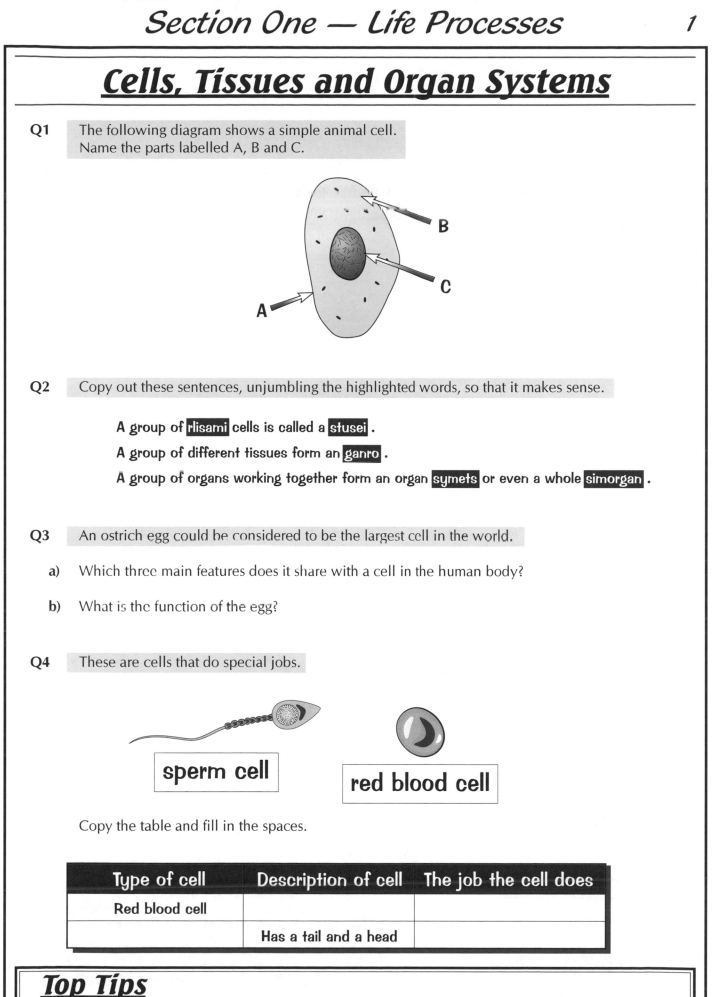

Q2   Copy out these sentences, unjumbling the highlighted words, so that it makes sense.

A group of **rlisami** cells is called a **stusei** .

A group of different tissues form an **ganro** .

A group of organs working together form an organ **symets** or even a whole **simorgan** .

Q3   An ostrich egg could be considered to be the largest cell in the world.

a)   Which three main features does it share with a cell in the human body?

b)   What is the function of the egg?

Q4   These are cells that do special jobs.

sperm cell

red blood cell

Copy the table and fill in the spaces.

Type of cell	Description of cell	The job the cell does
Red blood cell		
	Has a tail and a head	

Top Tips

Specialised cells are just cells with <u>jobs to do</u>. Exams are bound to ask you what that job is, or what makes the cell so good at it. Look at all the bits of the cell, and see where they're different — the shape's a good place to start.

The Digestive System

Q1   The diagrams below show the major parts of the digestive system.

D shows the mouth, salivary glands and the oesophagus.

Identify the other labelled parts, and write down their letter and name.

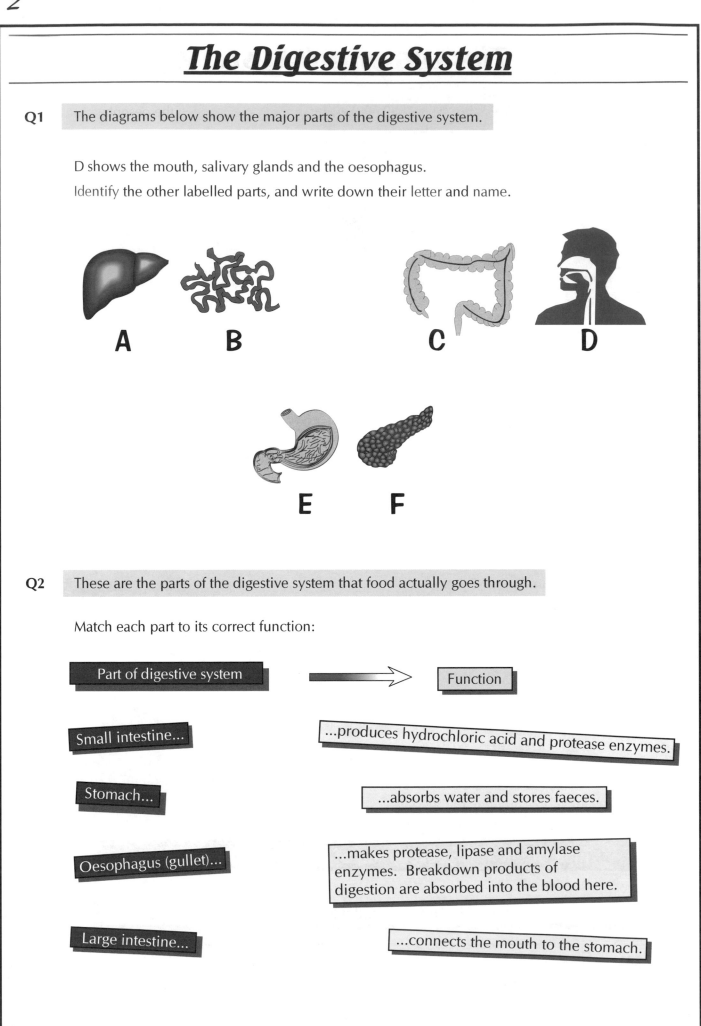

A   **B**   **C**   **D**

E   **F**

Q2   These are the parts of the digestive system that food actually goes through.

Match each part to its correct function:

Part of digestive system   →   Function

Small intestine...

...produces hydrochloric acid and protease enzymes.

Stomach...

...absorbs water and stores faeces.

Oesophagus (gullet)...

...makes protease, lipase and amylase enzymes. Breakdown products of digestion are absorbed into the blood here.

Large intestine...

...connects the mouth to the stomach.

The Digestive System

Q3 Look at the diagram below. It shows food moving through the inside of the oesophagus.

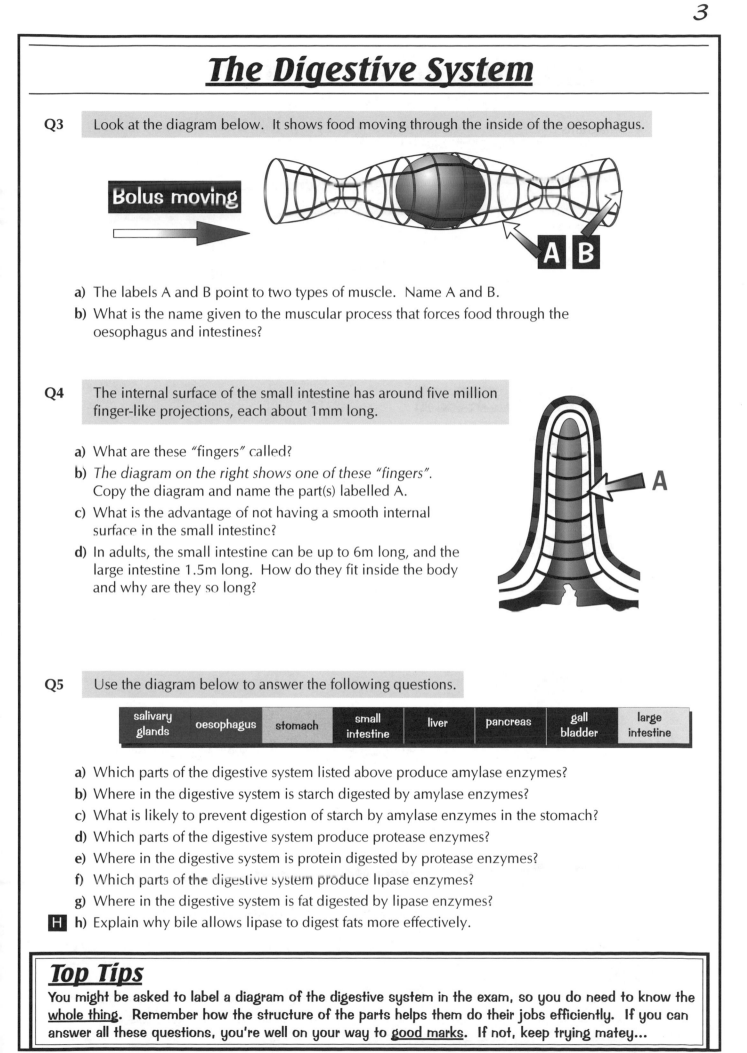

Bolus moving

A B

a) The labels A and B point to two types of muscle. Name A and B.
b) What is the name given to the muscular process that forces food through the oesophagus and intestines?

Q4 The internal surface of the small intestine has around five million finger-like projections, each about 1mm long.

a) What are these "fingers" called?
b) *The diagram on the right shows one of these "fingers".* Copy the diagram and name the part(s) labelled A.
c) What is the advantage of not having a smooth internal surface in the small intestine?
d) In adults, the small intestine can be up to 6m long, and the large intestine 1.5m long. How do they fit inside the body and why are they so long?

A

Q5 Use the diagram below to answer the following questions.

salivary glands	oesophagus	stomach	small intestine	liver	pancreas	gall bladder	large intestine

a) Which parts of the digestive system listed above produce amylase enzymes?
b) Where in the digestive system is starch digested by amylase enzymes?
c) What is likely to prevent digestion of starch by amylase enzymes in the stomach?
d) Which parts of the digestive system produce protease enzymes?
e) Where in the digestive system is protein digested by protease enzymes?
f) Which parts of the digestive system produce lipase enzymes?
g) Where in the digestive system is fat digested by lipase enzymes?
H h) Explain why bile allows lipase to digest fats more effectively.

Top Tips
You might be asked to label a diagram of the digestive system in the exam, so you do need to know the <u>whole thing</u>. Remember how the structure of the parts helps them do their jobs efficiently. If you can answer all these questions, you're well on your way to <u>good marks</u>. If not, keep trying matey...

Diffusion of "Food" Molecules

Q1 Which of the following food groups is the best source of protein?

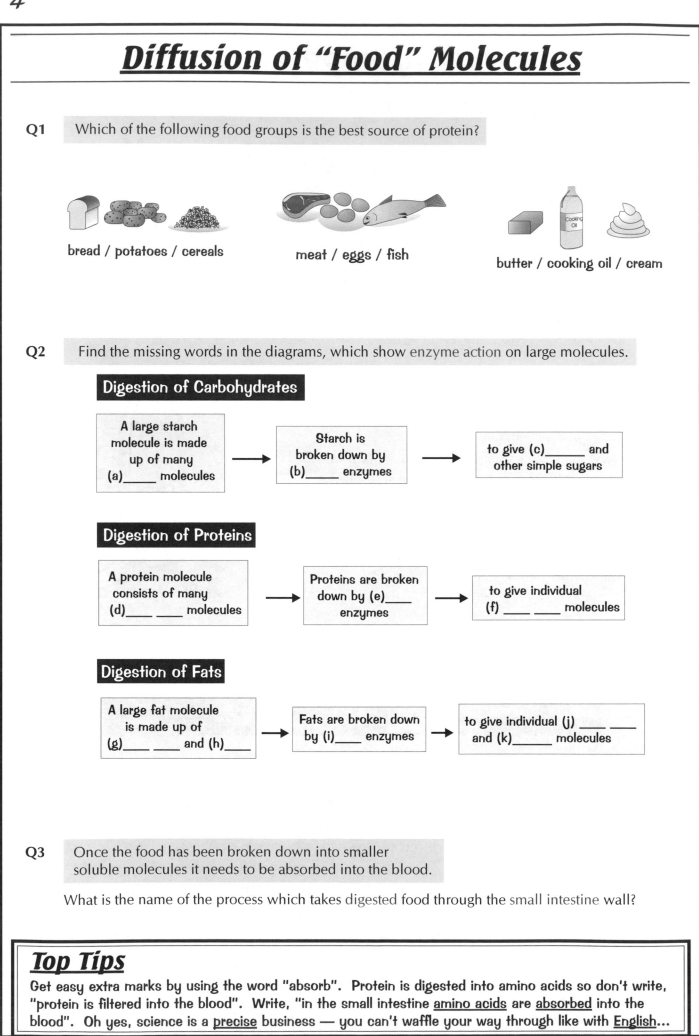

bread / potatoes / cereals   meat / eggs / fish   butter / cooking oil / cream

Q2 Find the missing words in the diagrams, which show enzyme action on large molecules.

Digestion of Carbohydrates

A large starch molecule is made up of many (a)_____ molecules → Starch is broken down by (b)_____ enzymes → to give (c)_____ and other simple sugars

Digestion of Proteins

A protein molecule consists of many (d)____ ____ molecules → Proteins are broken down by (e)____ enzymes → to give individual (f) ____ ____ molecules

Digestion of Fats

A large fat molecule is made up of (g)____ ____ and (h)____ → Fats are broken down by (i)____ enzymes → to give individual (j) ____ ____ and (k)_____ molecules

Q3 Once the food has been broken down into smaller soluble molecules it needs to be absorbed into the blood.

What is the name of the process which takes digested food through the small intestine wall?

Top Tips

Get easy extra marks by using the word "absorb". Protein is digested into amino acids so don't write, "protein is filtered into the blood". Write, "in the small intestine <u>amino acids</u> are <u>absorbed</u> into the blood". Oh yes, science is a <u>precise</u> business — you can't waffle your way through like with <u>English</u>...

Section One — Life Processes

Blood

Q1   There are about five million red blood cells in each 1mm³ of blood. That's a lot!

What is the function of red blood cells?

Q2   Platelets are small fragments of cells. Like red cells, they do not have a nucleus, but they are only about a third of the size of a red cell. There is one platelet to every 12 red cells in the blood. That's a lot too.

What is the function of platelets?

Q3   There is one white cell to every 600 red cells in the blood. That's still quite a lot! White cells are involved in protecting the body against infection, and don't just occur in the blood.

a)   Give three ways in which white cells protect us against infection.

b)   Where else in the body might you find white cells?

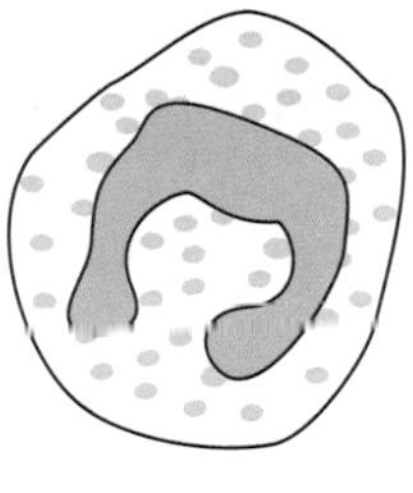

Q4   Plasma is important because the red cells, platelets and white cells are suspended in it.

One other important function of plasma is transport. What substances does plasma transport? Choose from the list below.

| products of digestion | hormones | antitoxins | oxygen | water |
| urea | dissolved mineral salts | carbon dioxide | antibodies |

Q5   Draw a summary table to show the functions of each of the four components of blood.

H Q6   Red blood cells have a doughnut shape (see diagram on the right).

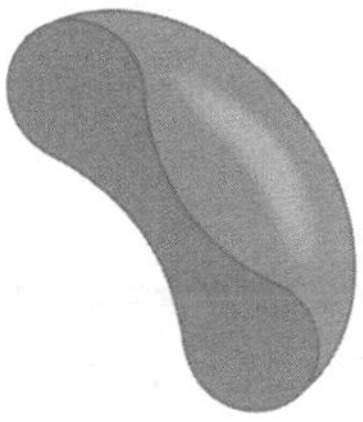

a)   Explain how this shape helps a red blood cell to carry out its function.

b)   Name the substance contained in red blood cells which allows them to carry oxygen. How does it work?

c)   Red blood cells in humans and most other mammals have no nucleus. How does this feature help a red blood cell carry out its function effectively?

Top Tips
Remember — there are <u>four</u> main components of blood. You need to know what they <u>look like</u> and what they <u>do</u>. It's not a lot of stuff to remember, but just be careful you don't get the bits mixed up.

Section One — Life Processes

The Nervous System

Q1 Match up the following sense organs with the receptors they contain.

Organs ⟹ Receptors

eyes have receptors	that are sensitive to pressure and temperature
ears have receptors	that are sensitive to light
the tongue and nose have receptors	that are sensitive to chemicals
the skin has receptors	that are sensitive to sound and changes in position

Q2 The diagram on the right shows the main features of the nervous system.

a) Name the parts of the nervous system labelled **X, Y** and **Z**.

b) When parts **X** and **Y** are taken together, they have a name. What is this name?

Q3 Copy and complete these sentences about neurones. Choose from the list of words below. You can use words more than once, if you need to.

| receptor | effector | spinal cord |

a) Sensory neurones carry nerve impulses from the .... to the ....

b) Motor neurones carry nerve impulses from the .... to the ....

Q4 The diagrams to the right show two types of neurone.

Copy the diagrams. Label as many features as you can in each diagram.

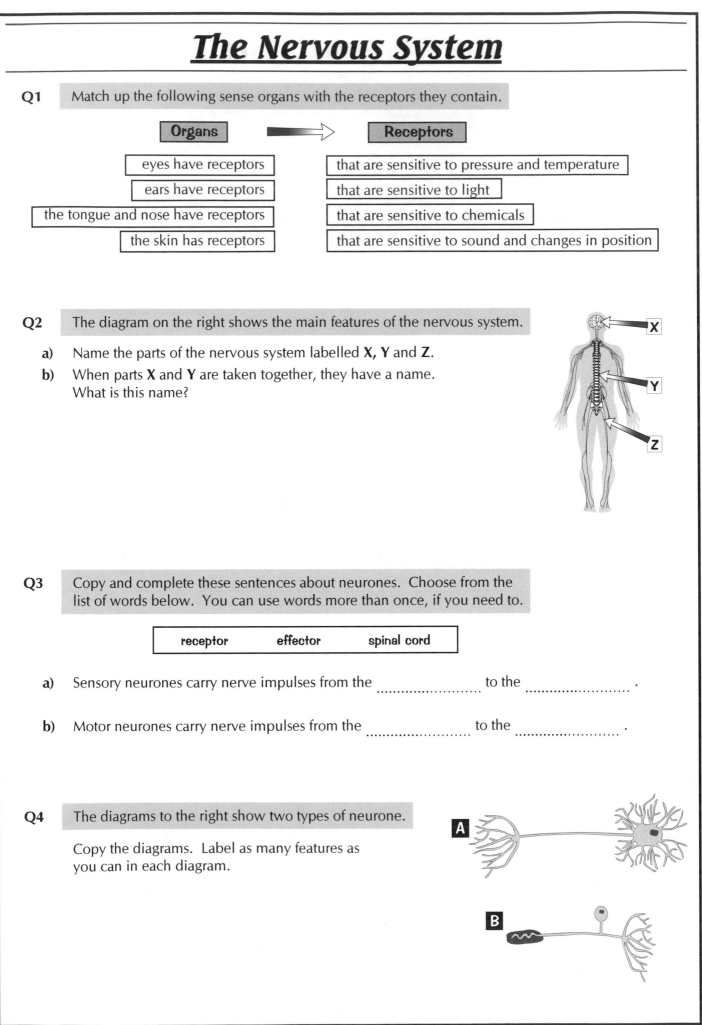

The Nervous System

H Q5 Copy these sentences about reflex actions, choosing the correct words from each underlined pair:

"A reflex action is an conscious / automatic response to a stimulus / receptor. It happens very quickly / slowly and involves / does not involve the brian / brain. Reflex actions allow us to coordinate body activity by remote control / nervous control."

H Q6 The diagram on the right shows a synapse greatly magnified.

a) Where do you find synapses? What is the function of a synapse?

b) What do the bubbles of chemical crossing the synapse do?

c) There are mitochondria in the diagram. What does this suggest about the working of a synapse?

d) Electrical wires can be joined together using solder, a junction box, or simply by twisting the ends together.

Suggest a reason why neurones cannot be connected together directly in this way.

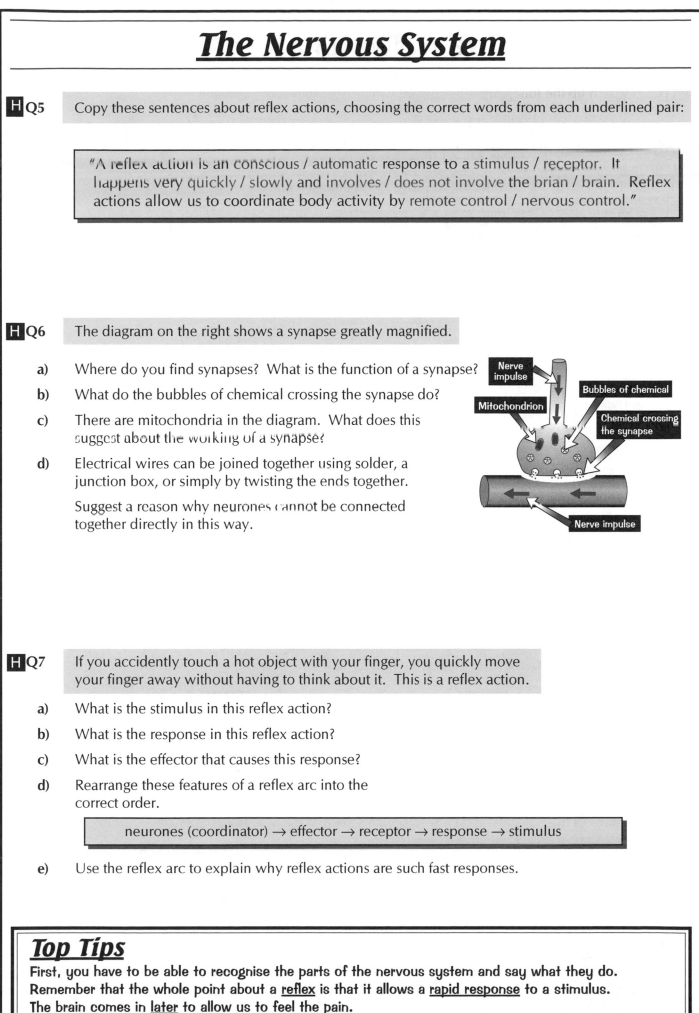

H Q7 If you accidently touch a hot object with your finger, you quickly move your finger away without having to think about it. This is a reflex action.

a) What is the stimulus in this reflex action?

b) What is the response in this reflex action?

c) What is the effector that causes this response?

d) Rearrange these features of a reflex arc into the correct order.

neurones (coordinator) → effector → receptor → response → stimulus

e) Use the reflex arc to explain why reflex actions are such fast responses.

Top Tips
First, you have to be able to recognise the parts of the nervous system and say what they do. Remember that the whole point about a <u>reflex</u> is that it allows a <u>rapid response</u> to a stimulus. The brain comes in <u>later</u> to allow us to feel the pain.

The Eye

Q1 Look at the diagram on the right.
It shows a section through an eye.

a) Match the names below to the parts of the eye labelled
A — H. Make a table for your answers.

ciliary muscles [ ] cornea [ ] pupil [ ]

iris [ ] retina [ ] lens [ ]

optic nerve [ ] suspensory ligaments [ ]

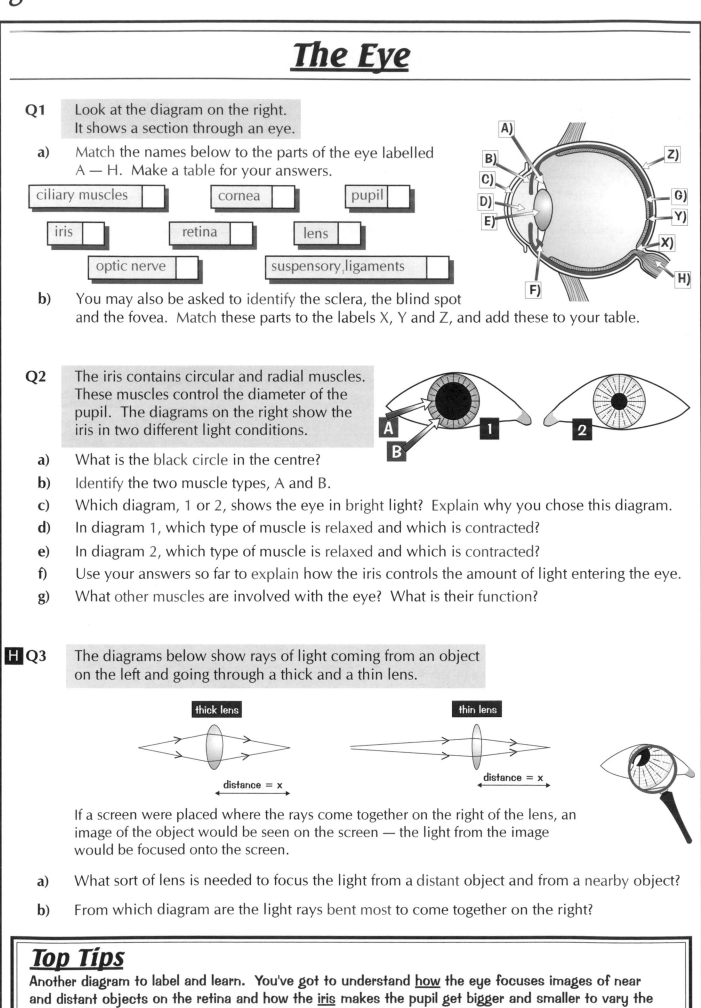

b) You may also be asked to identify the sclera, the blind spot
and the fovea. Match these parts to the labels X, Y and Z, and add these to your table.

Q2 The iris contains circular and radial muscles.
These muscles control the diameter of the
pupil. The diagrams on the right show the
iris in two different light conditions.

a) What is the black circle in the centre?

b) Identify the two muscle types, A and B.

c) Which diagram, 1 or 2, shows the eye in bright light? Explain why you chose this diagram.

d) In diagram 1, which type of muscle is relaxed and which is contracted?

e) In diagram 2, which type of muscle is relaxed and which is contracted?

f) Use your answers so far to explain how the iris controls the amount of light entering the eye.

g) What other muscles are involved with the eye? What is their function?

H Q3 The diagrams below show rays of light coming from an object
on the left and going through a thick and a thin lens.

thick lens

thin lens

distance = x

distance = x

If a screen were placed where the rays come together on the right of the lens, an
image of the object would be seen on the screen — the light from the image
would be focused onto the screen.

a) What sort of lens is needed to focus the light from a distant object and from a nearby object?

b) From which diagram are the light rays bent most to come together on the right?

Top Tips

Another diagram to label and learn. You've got to understand <u>how</u> the eye focuses images of near
and distant objects on the retina and how the <u>iris</u> makes the pupil get bigger and smaller to vary the
amount of light.

Hormones

Q1   Copy and complete the following sentences by adding the most suitable words from the box:

receptors	hormones	systems	glands
nervous system	bloodstream	chemicals	

Many processes within the body are coordinated by _____ called

_____ . These substances are produced by _____ and

transported to their target organs by the _____ .

Q2   Copy and complete the following table.

Name of hormone	Gland	Function
a) Insulin		turns glucose to glycogen
b)	Pancreas	turns glycogen to glucose
c) Oestrogen		develops female sexual characteristics
d) Follicle Stimulating Hormone (FSH)		causes eggs to mature and ovaries to produce oestrogen

Q3   The bloodstream provides the method of transport that enables hormones to reach their target organ.

a)   Using the labels below, copy and complete the diagram opposite showing the production and action of hormones in the body.

endocrine gland   response

target organ   bloodstream

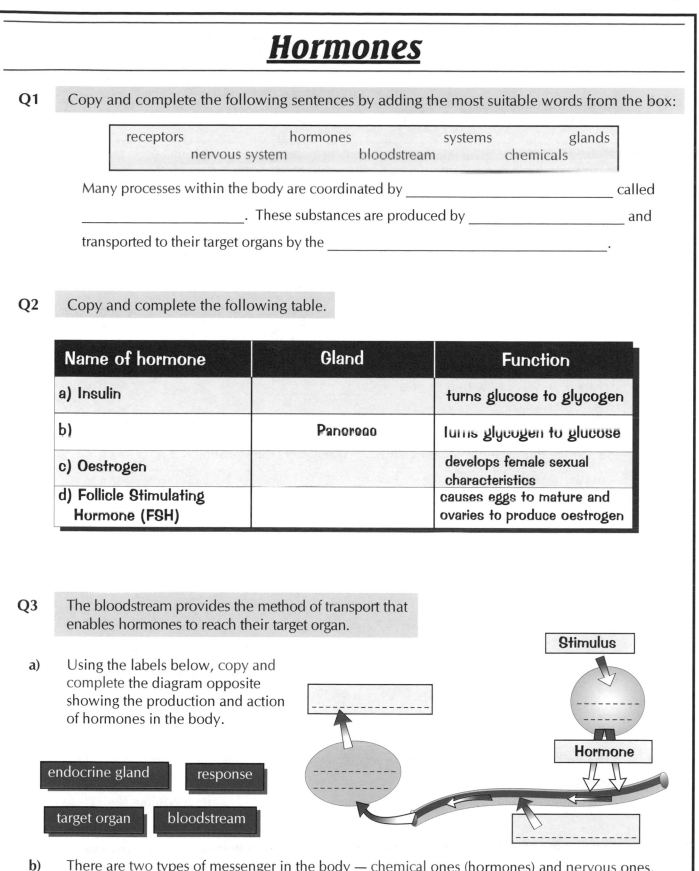

b)   There are two types of messenger in the body — chemical ones (hormones) and nervous ones. Name four differences between the two types. (Think about the speed of the message and the way they act.)

The Menstrual Cycle

Q1 Copy and complete these sentences using words from the box to describe what happens to the uterus during the menstrual cycle.

You can use the words more than once or not at all.

breaks down	maintained	menstruation	builds up	fertilised egg.

a) On day 1, the bleeding starts.

The lining of the uterus

_____.

This is known as _____.

Days 1   4   14   28

(a)   (b)   (c)

b) From day 4 to 14, the lining of the uterus _____ again into a thick spongy layer

of blood vessels, ready to receive a _____.

c) The wall is then maintained until day 28. If no _____ has landed there by then,

the spongy lining begins to break down and the cycle begins again.

Q2 Menstruation is controlled by three main hormones.
Name the two places where they are produced.

Q3 Copy the table opposite and fill in the parts labelled **i)** to **iii)**.

Hormone Name	Source	Function
FSH (Follicle Stimulating Hormone)	Pituitary	i)
Oestrogen	Ovaries	ii)
iii)	Pituitary	Stimulates the release of an egg

Q4 "The Pill" is a contraceptive taken by women that works by controlling egg production.

a) Which hormones does the pill contain?
b) What effect does taking the pill regularly have on the level of oestrogen in the body?

Maintaining oestrogen at this level inhibits production of FSH.

c) After a period of time, what effect would this have on egg production?
d) Would you expect the egg production of someone on the pill to return to normal after they stopped taking it? Why?

Q5 Are the levels of oestrogen and FSH usually controlled by a feedback mechanism? Explain your answer.

Homeostasis

Q1   What does the word homeostasis mean?

Q2   The body produces two main waste substances that it needs to get rid of.

  a)   Name these two substances.

  b)   For each, say which process produces them and which organ excretes them from the body.

Q3   The diagram opposite shows some of the body's main organs.

     Name each of the organs A – H in the diagram.

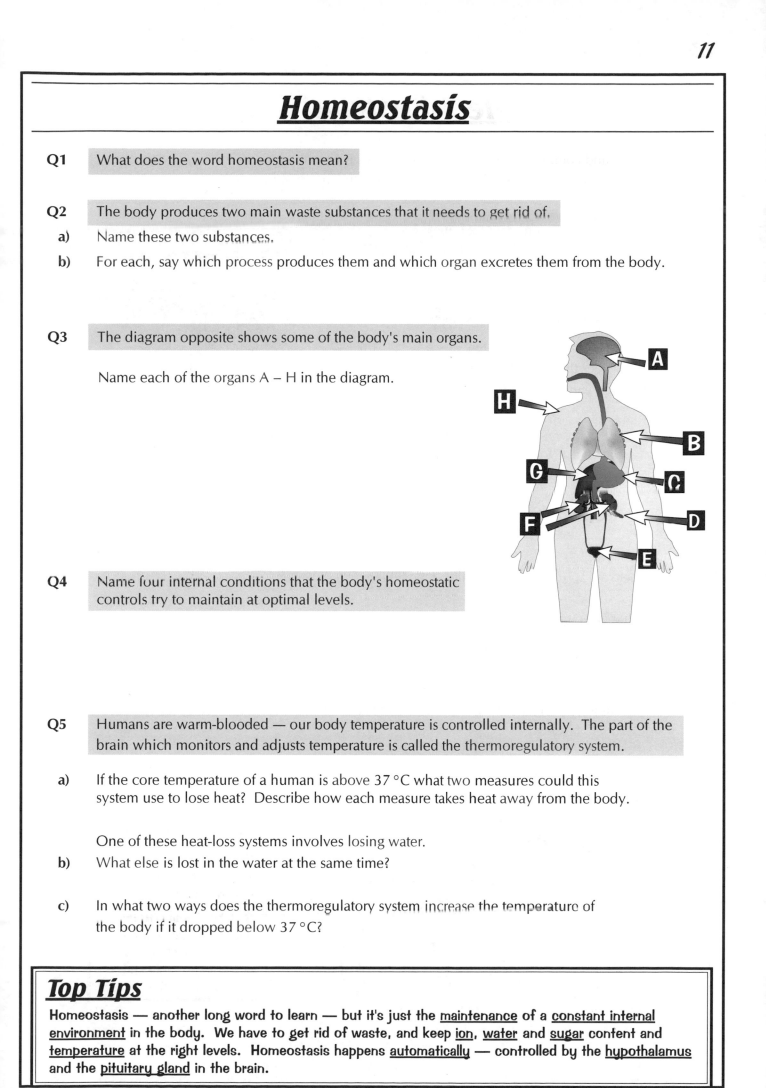

Q4   Name four internal conditions that the body's homeostatic controls try to maintain at optimal levels.

Q5   Humans are warm-blooded — our body temperature is controlled internally. The part of the brain which monitors and adjusts temperature is called the thermoregulatory system.

  a)   If the core temperature of a human is above 37 °C what two measures could this system use to lose heat? Describe how each measure takes heat away from the body.

     One of these heat-loss systems involves losing water.

  b)   What else is lost in the water at the same time?

  c)   In what two ways does the thermoregulatory system increase the temperature of the body if it dropped below 37 °C?

Top Tips

Homeostasis — another long word to learn — but it's just the <u>maintenance</u> of a <u>constant internal environment</u> in the body. We have to get rid of waste, and keep <u>ion</u>, <u>water</u> and <u>sugar</u> content and <u>temperature</u> at the right levels. Homeostasis happens <u>automatically</u> — controlled by the <u>hypothalamus</u> and the <u>pituitary gland</u> in the brain.

Kidneys

Q1 The kidneys are the body's filters. They adjust the levels of various substances in the blood and remove ones we don't need.

  a) What are the three main roles of the kidneys?
  b) What does the word excretion mean?

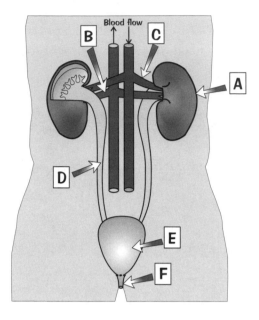

Q2 The diagram on the right shows part of the system involving the kidneys.

  a) Name the parts of the system A – F .
  b) How does the blood travelling through parts B and C differ?

H Q3 There are approximately a million tube systems in a kidney.

  a) What is the name given to these tube systems?

  b) What surrounds each of them?

  c) Below is a diagram of a single tube system.
    The table opposite contains a description of each labelled part.

    Match the labels **a) – c)** with their correct description 1 – 3.

| 1. Branch of renal vein taking away filtered blood. |
| 2. Branch of the renal artery — blood here requires "cleaning". |
| 3. Tubes leading to the bladder — carry away urine, the waste liquid consisting of urea and excess ions and water. |

Disease in Humans

Q1 Answer these microbe questions:

a) Name the two different types of microbe.

b) In what conditions do most everyday microbes tend to live and multiply well?

c) What effects can microbes have in our bodies?

Q2 Name the two different types of microbes shown opposite.

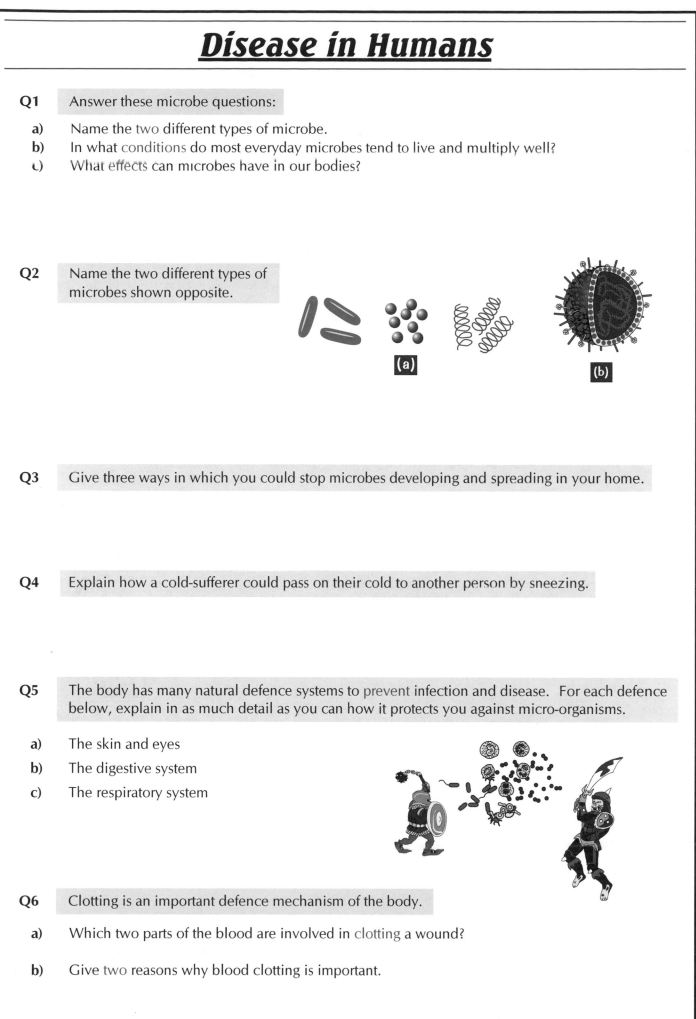

(a)   (b)

Q3 Give three ways in which you could stop microbes developing and spreading in your home.

Q4 Explain how a cold-sufferer could pass on their cold to another person by sneezing.

Q5 The body has many natural defence systems to prevent infection and disease. For each defence below, explain in as much detail as you can how it protects you against micro-organisms.

a) The skin and eyes

b) The digestive system

c) The respiratory system

Q6 Clotting is an important defence mechanism of the body.

a) Which two parts of the blood are involved in clotting a wound?

b) Give two reasons why blood clotting is important.

Disease in Humans

Q7   If bacteria enter the body, special blood cells respond automatically.

Which type of blood cell attack invading bacteria?
Explain the three lines of attack these cells have against invaders.

Q8   In an experiment, somebody was injected with microbes. After 20 days they had produced 1 unit of antibody. After a few months, they were injected again with the same type of microbe. This time, they produced 2.5 units of antibody after 17 days.

a)   Copy out the sentence below, choosing the correct words from each underlinesd pair.

When you are exposed to a microbe for the second time, the

production of antibodies is **slower** / **faster** than the first time,

and **more** / **less** antibody is produced than the first time.

b)   When you are vaccinated against a microbe that causes disease, you are usually injected with dead or damaged microbes, or parts of the microbe.

Explain how vaccinations protect you from microbes that cause disease.

Q9   Copy and complete the following paragraph using words from the box.

antibiotic   chemicals   kills   bacteria

Antibiotics only work on .... Some medicines that are not

.... work by suppressing the symptoms of the illness.

Symptoms are the body's response to the waste .... made and

the damage caused by the microbes. An antibiotic ....

microbes that cause the symptoms.

Good Lord! That's no microbe, that's Gerald with a phoney moustache!

Q10   Answer these questions about antibiotics.

a)   Why do antibiotics not work on all bacteria?

b)   Why do doctors try to limit the use of antibiotics?

c)   Why would antibiotics not help you if you had the flu?

Top Tips   This is an important section — not just for your exams but also for helping you to understand how you can keep healthy. You've got to know your <u>enemy</u> (the different types of micro-organisms), the ways that your body <u>defends</u> against them, and what you can do to <u>help</u>. It's just war games on a tiny tiny scale — if you like that sort of thing.

Drugs

Q1   Drugs are classified as chemicals which can affect human behaviour.

Name three of the main groups of drugs.

Q2   Copy and complete the table below, showing the effects of different types of drugs on the nervous system.

Drug type	Effect on brain and rest of nervous system	Examples of drug type
Sedatives	(a) --------------------------	Valium / barbiturates
(b) -------------	Speed up the brain and increase alertness	Ecstasy / cocaine milder drug (c) ----------------
(d) -------------	Reduce sense of pain	Paracetamol / heroin

Q3   Give two reasons why drugs are dangerous.

Q4   What do the following words mean in relation to drugs?

a)   addiction
b)   withdrawal

Q5   Drugs come in all shapes and forms — not just tablets and pills. This is evident with solvents.

a)   What are solvents?
b)   Why do we often refer to solvent abuse as "glue-sniffing"?
c)   What are the four main organs that glue-sniffing affects?
d)   What symptoms may a glue-sniffer display?

Q6   Answer these questions about painkillers:

a)   Name two examples of painkillers.
b)   Heroin is a particularly dangerous form of painkiller because it is very addictive.
     What problems can this drug cause?

Top Tips   You need to know <u>how</u> the main types of drugs affect the body. Remember that painkillers, tranquillisers and sleeping pills help ill people, but are often <u>abused</u>.
When the body has got <u>used</u> to the <u>effects</u> of a drug, <u>painful</u> and <u>unpleasant withdrawal symptoms</u> happen when the person tries to stop taking the drug — which creates physical <u>addiction</u>.

Section One — Life Processes

Drugs

Q7 Quite apart from its effect on a person's behaviour, alcohol consumption can severely affect the body's ability to function properly.

a) What system in the body is most affected by alcohol in the short term?

b) What are the short-term effects of moderate alcohol consumption?

c) Why is drinking and driving a stupid combination?

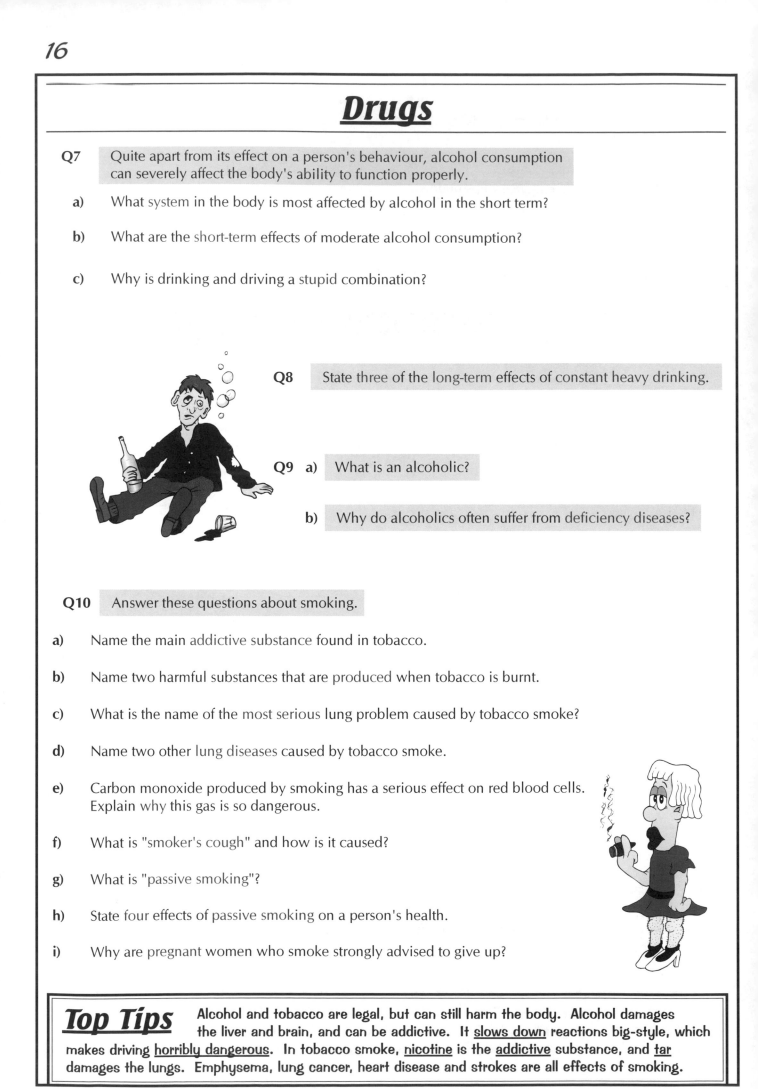

Q8 State three of the long-term effects of constant heavy drinking.

Q9 a) What is an alcoholic?

b) Why do alcoholics often suffer from deficiency diseases?

Q10 Answer these questions about smoking.

a) Name the main addictive substance found in tobacco.

b) Name two harmful substances that are produced when tobacco is burnt.

c) What is the name of the most serious lung problem caused by tobacco smoke?

d) Name two other lung diseases caused by tobacco smoke.

e) Carbon monoxide produced by smoking has a serious effect on red blood cells. Explain why this gas is so dangerous.

f) What is "smoker's cough" and how is it caused?

g) What is "passive smoking"?

h) State four effects of passive smoking on a person's health.

i) Why are pregnant women who smoke strongly advised to give up?

Top Tips Alcohol and tobacco are legal, but can still harm the body. Alcohol damages the liver and brain, and can be addictive. It <u>slows down</u> reactions big-style, which makes driving <u>horribly dangerous</u>. In tobacco smoke, <u>nicotine</u> is the <u>addictive</u> substance, and <u>tar</u> damages the lungs. Emphysema, lung cancer, heart disease and strokes are all effects of smoking.

Variation in Plants and Animals

Q1   When Alex looked at the ivy plant growing up the oak tree in his back
garden, he was surprised how much the size and colour of the leaves varied.

    a)   What kind of variation is this?

    b)   What can affect the size and colour of ivy leaves?

    c)   Ivy plants have a very distinctive shape to their leaves.
All mature leaves have the same shape.
Is this genetically or environmentally determined?

Q2   Identical twins have the same genes, so they are genetically identical.
The table shows four people, identified by the letters a, b, c and d.

    a)   Use the information in the table to identify
which two people are identical twins.

    b)   Explain your answer.

Characteristic	Person a	Person b	Person c	Person d
Have a sun tan	✔	✔		
They are male	✔	✔	✔	
They are female				✔
Can tongue roll	✔		✔	
Normal hair colour is brown	✔	✔	✔	✔
Have bleached white hair			✔	✔
Have brown eyes	✔	✔	✔	

Q3   Copy the table below and place ticks in it to give the
correct information for each of the human characteristics.

Characteristic (human)	Affected by Environment Yes	No
Birth weight		
Skin colour		
Blood group		
Hand span		
Eye colour		
Haemophilia		

Top Tips The most important thing for you to get your head round here is what is caused by
<u>genes</u> and what is caused by the <u>environment</u>. Remember that identical twins don't have to look
completely identical — they could look different in terms of suntans, weight, dyed hair, scars, etc...

Mitosis and Meiosis

H Q1   Copy out the table below and use the following words to complete the blanks.

asexual	exact	gametes	parent	reduction	two

Mitosis is a process used during growth and _____ reproduction. Each chromosome in the original cell makes an _____ copy of itself. When this type of division is complete, _____ daughter cells are produced, each having the same chromosome number as the _____ cell. Meiosis is a _____ division — this means that the number of chromosomes in the original cell is reduced (halved). This process is used in the production of male and female _____. Meiosis involves some jumbling of genetic material, so producing variation.

H Q2   State whether the following statements apply to meiosis or mitosis.

a) Produces **haploid** cells.

b) Produces identical cells to **parent** cell.

c) At the end of division, two **daughter** cells are produced.

d) Used in **sexual** reproduction.

e) Used in **asexual** reproduction.

H Q3   The diagram below shows the difference between the two types of cell division.

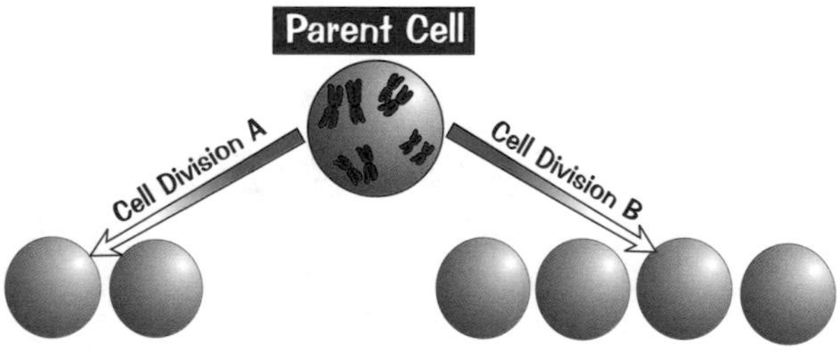

Parent Cell

Cell Division A

Cell Division B

a)   Name the type of cell division involved in A and B.

b)   Where does A take place in the human body?

c)   Where does B take place in the human body?

d)   If the diagram represents cell division in the human body, how many chromosomes are there in one of the cells produced from:
i) division A?
ii) division B?

Mitosis and Meiosis

H Q4   Diagram A below shows the stages involved in cell reproduction by mitosis.
Describe in your own words what is happening at each of the numbered stages.

Q5   Diagram B shows the stages involved in cell reproduction by meiosis.
Describe in your own words what is happening at each of the numbered stages.

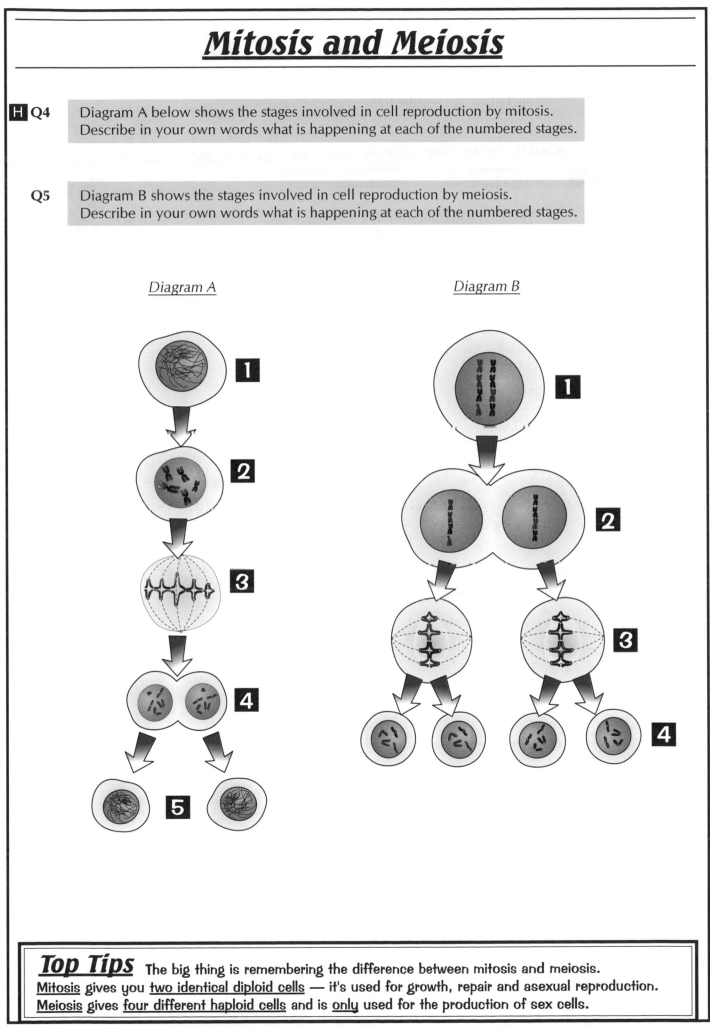

Diagram A   Diagram B

Top Tips The big thing is remembering the difference between mitosis and meiosis.
Mitosis gives you two identical diploid cells — it's used for growth, repair and asexual reproduction.
Meiosis gives four different haploid cells and is only used for the production of sex cells.

Fertilisation: The Meeting of Gametes

Q1   The diagram shows the progress from sex cells to a baby.

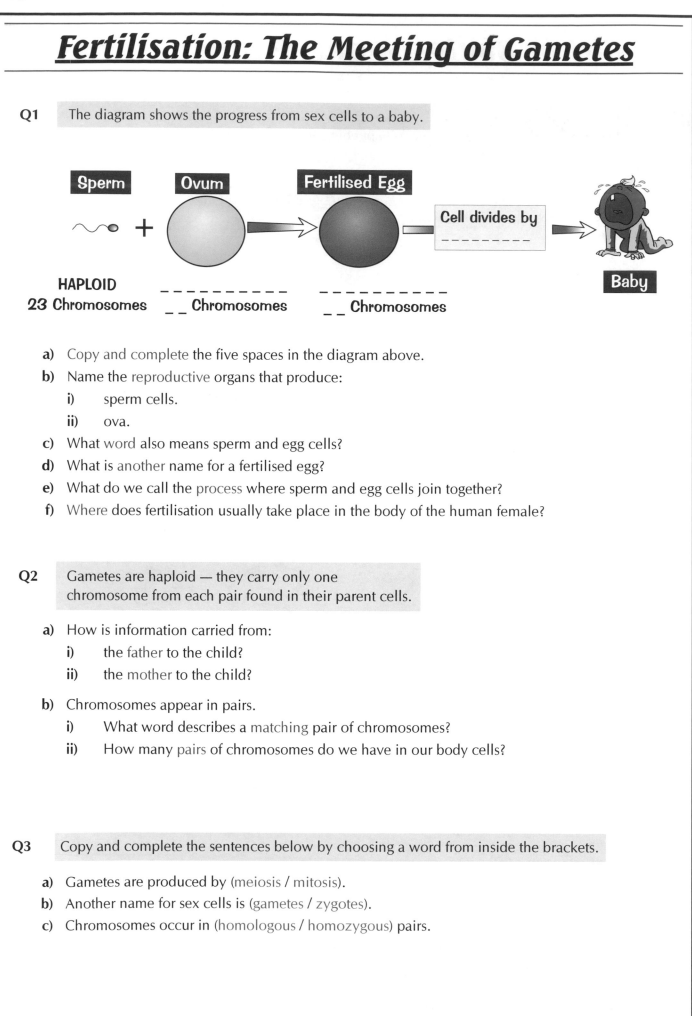

Sperm   **Ovum**   **Fertilised Egg**

Cell divides by
_ _ _ _ _ _ _ _

Baby

HAPLOID
23 Chromosomes   _ _ Chromosomes   _ _ Chromosomes

a)   Copy and complete the five spaces in the diagram above.

b)   Name the reproductive organs that produce:

    i)   sperm cells.

    ii)   ova.

c)   What word also means sperm and egg cells?

d)   What is another name for a fertilised egg?

e)   What do we call the process where sperm and egg cells join together?

f)   Where does fertilisation usually take place in the body of the human female?

Q2   Gametes are haploid — they carry only one
chromosome from each pair found in their parent cells.

a)   How is information carried from:

    i)   the father to the child?

    ii)   the mother to the child?

b)   Chromosomes appear in pairs.

    i)   What word describes a matching pair of chromosomes?

    ii)   How many pairs of chromosomes do we have in our body cells?

Q3   Copy and complete the sentences below by choosing a word from inside the brackets.

a)   Gametes are produced by (meiosis / mitosis).

b)   Another name for sex cells is (gametes / zygotes).

c)   Chromosomes occur in (homologous / homozygous) pairs.

Girl or Boy? — X and Y Chromosomes

Q1 Chromosomes A and B (shown below) are pairs of sex chromosomes.

a) Which chromosome is male and which is female?

b) Where are chromosomes A and B found in the body?

c) What are male gametes and female gametes called?

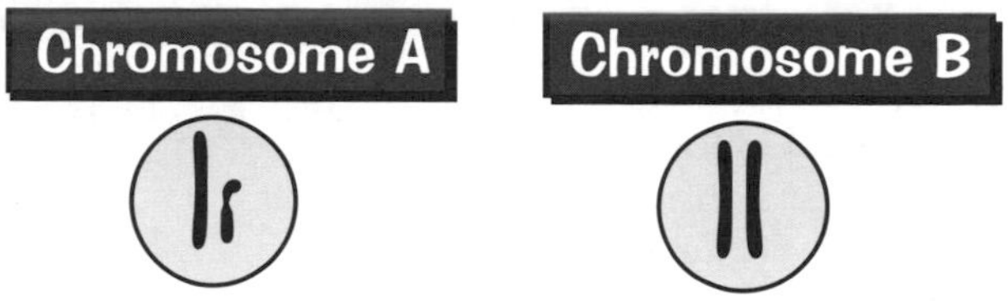

Chromosome A   **Chromosome B**

H Q2 Answer these questions:

a) Copy and complete the diagram, which shows possible ways that sex is inherited.

Parents' Phenotype : _____   _____

Parents' Genotype :   X X   X _

Gametes' Genotype :   X   X   X   _

Children's Genotype : _ _ X Y   X X _ _

Children's Phenotype : ____ ____   ____ ____

b) Work out from the diagram the ratio of boys to girls.

c) A couple have one child, Janet.
The couple are convinced that their next child will be a boy because they already have a daughter. Is this true? Explain your answer.

d) Genotypes of offspring can also be worked out with a checkerboard type diagram (sometimes called a Punnett Square).
Copy and complete the diagram to the right.

Female Gametes X   X   X   Y   **Male Gametes**

H Q3 In the old days, kings sometimes beheaded their wives for not giving them sons.

a) What sex chromosomes do sperm cells have?

b) What sex chromosomes do egg cells have?

c) i) Is it the man's or woman's gametes that determine the sex of the child?

ii) Explain your answer.

Chop off her head!!

Top Tips You know the basic point that fertilisation is when a sperm and an egg cell fuse together, but remember that two <u>haploid</u> cells are fusing together to form a <u>diploid</u> cell. Don't forget that <u>after</u> fertilisation, this cell is called a <u>zygote</u> — a funny name, but you need to know it.

Monohybrid Crosses

Q1   On the right is a genetic diagram showing how two
pea plants could share their genes by cross-fertilisation.

a) What do we mean by:
   i)   phenotype?
   ii)   genotype?
b) What do we mean by "F1 generation"?
c) What is the ratio of their:
   i)   genotypes?
   ii)   phenotypes?
d) Give all the possible genotypes
    from the alleles T and t.
e) What are the possible phenotypes
    from these alleles?

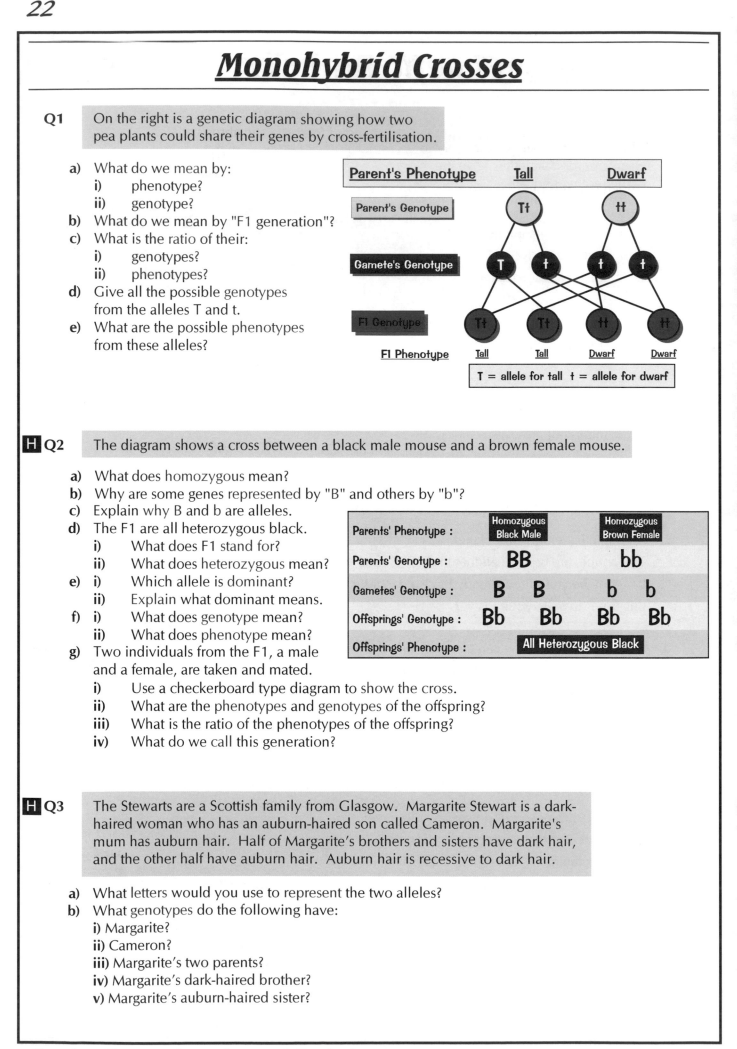

H Q2   The diagram shows a cross between a black male mouse and a brown female mouse.

a) What does homozygous mean?
b) Why are some genes represented by "B" and others by "b"?
c) Explain why B and b are alleles.
d) The F1 are all heterozygous black.
   i)   What does F1 stand for?
   ii)   What does heterozygous mean?
e) i)   Which allele is dominant?
   ii)   Explain what dominant means.
f) i)   What does genotype mean?
   ii)   What does phenotype mean?
g) Two individuals from the F1, a male
    and a female, are taken and mated.
   i)   Use a checkerboard type diagram to show the cross.
   ii)   What are the phenotypes and genotypes of the offspring?
   iii) What is the ratio of the phenotypes of the offspring?
   iv)   What do we call this generation?

H Q3   The Stewarts are a Scottish family from Glasgow. Margarite Stewart is a dark-
haired woman who has an auburn-haired son called Cameron. Margarite's
mum has auburn hair. Half of Margarite's brothers and sisters have dark hair,
and the other half have auburn hair. Auburn hair is recessive to dark hair.

a) What letters would you use to represent the two alleles?
b) What genotypes do the following have:
    i) Margarite?
    ii) Cameron?
    iii) Margarite's two parents?
    iv) Margarite's dark-haired brother?
    v) Margarite's auburn-haired sister?

Section Two — Genetics and Evolution

Genetic Disorders

Q1 The diagram shows a family who have been tested for the cystic fibrosis allele.

a) Using appropriate letters, give the genotypes of the mother and father.
b) Will any of the children be sufferers?
c) i) Can you say which children will carry a recessive allele?
   ii) Explain your answer.
d) What is the chance of Beth being a carrier?
e) What proportion of their children are likely to be normal (i.e. not sufferers or carriers)?
f) i) From the diagram, can we tell whether both of the father's parents were carriers?
   ii) Explain your answer.

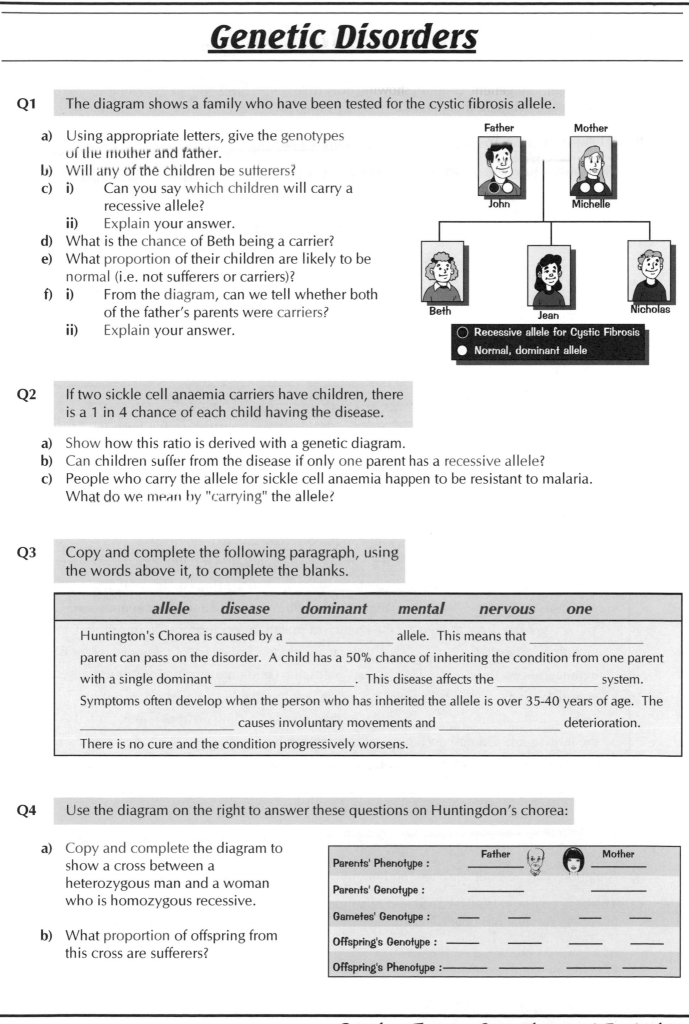

Recessive allele for Cystic Fibrosis
Normal, dominant allele

Q2 If two sickle cell anaemia carriers have children, there is a 1 in 4 chance of each child having the disease.

a) Show how this ratio is derived with a genetic diagram.
b) Can children suffer from the disease if only one parent has a recessive allele?
c) People who carry the allele for sickle cell anaemia happen to be resistant to malaria. What do we mean by "carrying" the allele?

Q3 Copy and complete the following paragraph, using the words above it, to complete the blanks.

allele	disease	dominant	mental	nervous	one

Huntington's Chorea is caused by a _____ allele. This means that _____ parent can pass on the disorder. A child has a 50% chance of inheriting the condition from one parent with a single dominant _____. This disease affects the _____ system. Symptoms often develop when the person who has inherited the allele is over 35-40 years of age. The _____ causes involuntary movements and _____ deterioration. There is no cure and the condition progressively worsens.

Q4 Use the diagram on the right to answer these questions on Huntingdon's chorea:

a) Copy and complete the diagram to show a cross between a heterozygous man and a woman who is homozygous recessive.

b) What proportion of offspring from this cross are sufferers?

	Father	Mother
Parents' Phenotype :	___	___
Parents' Genotype :	___	___
Gametes' Genotype :	___ ___	___ ___
Offspring's Genotype :	___ ___	___ ___
Offspring's Phenotype :	___ ___	___ ___

Mutations

Q1   Cells A and B are taken from two different Drosophila flies (fruit flies). One cell is normal, but the other has a mutation which gives the fly misshapen eyes. Cell A has the mutant gene.

a)   What is a gene?

b)   How can mutations like this one arise?

c)   Can you tell from the information given if the fly's offspring have the mutation?

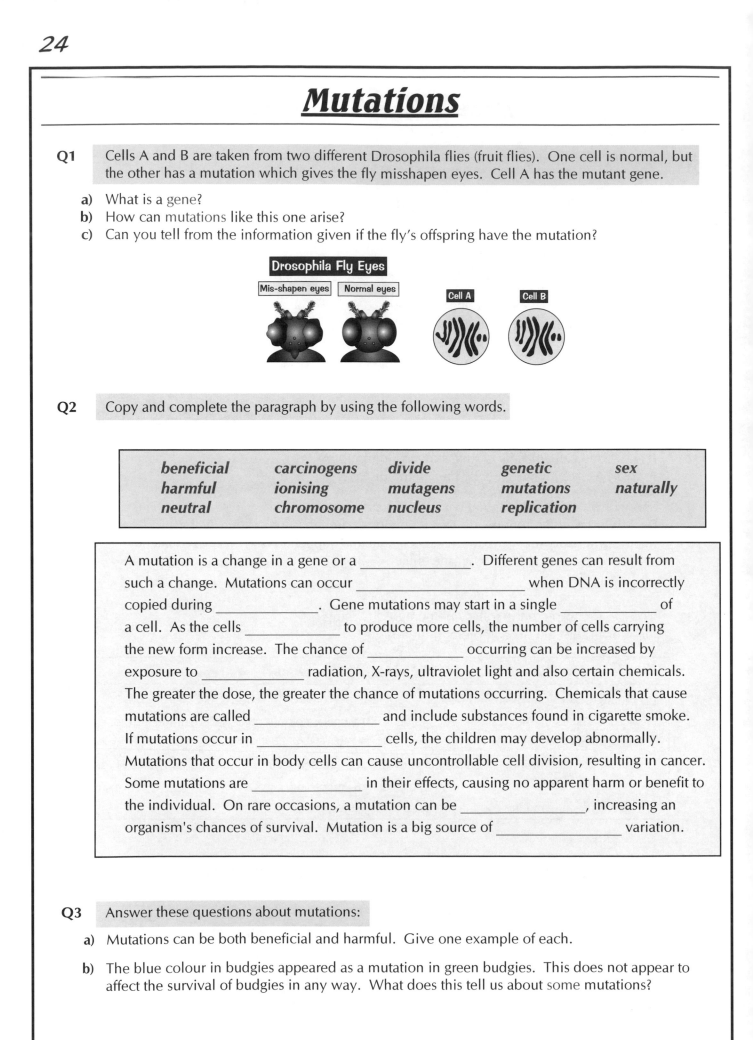

Q2   Copy and complete the paragraph by using the following words.

beneficial	*carcinogens*	*divide*	*genetic*	*sex*
harmful	*ionising*	*mutagens*	*mutations*	*naturally*
neutral	*chromosome*	*nucleus*	*replication*	

A mutation is a change in a gene or a _____. Different genes can result from such a change. Mutations can occur _____ when DNA is incorrectly copied during _____. Gene mutations may start in a single _____ of a cell. As the cells _____ to produce more cells, the number of cells carrying the new form increase. The chance of _____ occurring can be increased by exposure to _____ radiation, X-rays, ultraviolet light and also certain chemicals. The greater the dose, the greater the chance of mutations occurring. Chemicals that cause mutations are called _____ and include substances found in cigarette smoke. If mutations occur in _____ cells, the children may develop abnormally. Mutations that occur in body cells can cause uncontrollable cell division, resulting in cancer. Some mutations are _____ in their effects, causing no apparent harm or benefit to the individual. On rare occasions, a mutation can be _____, increasing an organism's chances of survival. Mutation is a big source of _____ variation.

Q3   Answer these questions about mutations:

a)   Mutations can be both beneficial and harmful. Give one example of each.

b)   The blue colour in budgies appeared as a mutation in green budgies. This does not appear to affect the survival of budgies in any way. What does this tell us about some mutations?

Natural Selection

Q1 The peppered moth is normally light in colour. Occasionally, a black variety appears. Insect eating birds like the thrush prey on these moths.

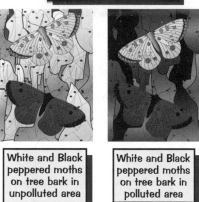

Peppered Moth

White and Black peppered moths on tree bark in unpolluted area

White and Black peppered moths on tree bark in polluted area

a) i) How does a black moth come about in a population of light coloured moths?

ii) How is the population of these moths kept constant?

b) *In 1848 the first black variety was noticed in Manchester. By 1895, 98% of the moth population of Manchester was black. During this time, the environment also became much more polluted, and darker as a result.*
Suggest why the number of black moths might have increased so dramatically between 1848 and 1895.

c) *Today, in industrialised areas, the population of dark moths is almost 100%. In Scotland and south-west England the reverse is true.*
Why does this happen?

d) Why is the black variety not a new species?

e) What is the name for the process that favours the members of a population that are best adapted to their environment?

Q2 Copy and complete the following sentences by choosing the correct words from the brackets.

a) The frequency of alleles which determine useful characteristics tend to (decrease / increase) in a population.

b) Factors like disease cause a population to (decrease / increase).

c) The organisms that are most likely to survive are those that are (best suited to their environment / strongest).

d) Survivors pass their genes on to their (offspring / partner).

e) Natural selection is an important process by which (evolution / mutation) takes place.

Top Tips: Natural selection — top theory. The <u>environment</u> selects characteristics that make individuals <u>survivors</u>. Survivors can <u>pass on</u> their <u>genes</u> to their children, who then pass them on to theirs and so on, and on — that's how evolution works.

Fossils and Evolution

Q1   Fossils in good condition are virtually only found in sedimentary rocks.

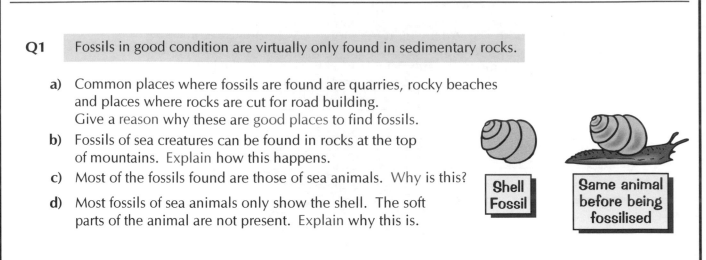

Shell Fossil

Same animal before being fossilised

a) Common places where fossils are found are quarries, rocky beaches and places where rocks are cut for road building. Give a reason why these are good places to find fossils.

b) Fossils of sea creatures can be found in rocks at the top of mountains. Explain how this happens.

c) Most of the fossils found are those of sea animals. Why is this?

d) Most fossils of sea animals only show the shell. The soft parts of the animal are not present. Explain why this is.

Q2   Choose the correct word or words from inside the brackets to complete the sentences.

a) In order for decay to occur, oxygen (is / is not) needed.

b) Most fossils form from hard parts of animals because they decay (quickly / slowly).

c) Fossilisation is most likely to occur (under the sea / on land).

d) The (higher / lower) in an undisturbed rock sequence a fossil is found, the older it is.

Q3   Place the sentences in order to explain the evolution of the giraffe.

~ Mutation and random variation resulted in some giraffes having longer necks than others.

~ The ancestors of the giraffes had short necks.

~ Natural selection resulted in more of the longer-necked offspring surviving (they could reach more food).

~ After a while, the only long-necked giraffes survived.

Q4   The diagram shows the earliest occurrence and abundance of fossil vertebrates.

a) Which were the first vertebrates to evolve?

b) Which were the last vertebrates to evolve?

c) How do fossils help us to understand evolution?

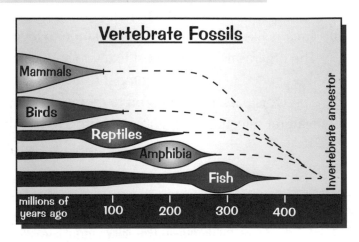

Vertebrate Fossils

Mammals

Birds

Reptiles

Amphibia

Fish

Invertebrate ancestor

millions of years ago   100   200   300   400

Section Two — Genetics and Evolution

Selective Breeding, etc.

Q1 Copy and complete the paragraph below, using the words in the box.

alleles	breed	characteristics	colours	ears	
milk	people	selective	variety	varieties	

Artificial selection is when _____ choose what characteristics to breed into living things. This can be used to produce new _____ and breeds of organisms. We choose the individuals which have _____ which are useful to us. We then _____ from these individuals. We choose individuals from the offspring which have the features useful to us, and breed from them. We repeat this over and over again. This is called _____ breeding. A use for selective breeding in agriculture is the production of varieties of plants and breeds of animals that produce greater yields or other desired characteristics. Examples of selective breeding in animals include the Fresian cow that produces greater _____ yields and dogs like the Basset hound that has droopy _____. Plants like wheat have been bred to grow bigger 'ears' with more grain. Also, new varieties of roses now exist with a wide range of flower _____ and shapes. Selective breeding, though, greatly reduces the number of _____ in a population (the gene pool) and therefore reduces _____ .

Q2 Choose the correct word from inside the brackets to complete the sentences.

a) Plants produced from cuttings grow into new plants by (meiotic / mitotic) cell division.

b) Tissue cultures are a useful way of producing large numbers of (different / identical) plants from a small number of cells.

c) Genetically identical plants are produced by (asexual / sexual) reproduction.

d) Growing plants from tissue cultures (decreases / increases) the size of the gene pool.

e) Cloning techniques are also used in producing identical animals by splitting embryo cells (after / before) they specialise.

Top Tips Selective breeding is when people select the characteristics they want to breed into plants and animals — it's very useful. You'll need to know examples of plants and animals that have been selectively bred. Don't forget the disadvantages, too.

Selective Breeding, etc.

Q3) Copy and complete the paragraph below, using the following words to fill in the blanks.

> *asexual   cells   cuttings   embryo   genetically   host*
> *identical   mitosis   naturally   splitting   tissue*

Clones are _____ identical organisms. These are produced in plants during _____ reproduction when _____ takes place. In plants, examples include reproduction by bulbs, stem tubers and runners, as well as _____.
Using _____ cultures also results in genetically _____ offspring (clones). This technique involves growing new plants from small groups of _____ from part of a plant. Cloning techniques are also used in producing identical cells in agriculture. This is done by _____ embryo cells (before they become specialised) from a developing animal _____ and then transplanting the identical embryos into a _____ mother. Clones are also produced _____, as in the case of identical twins.

Q4) The diagram shows a method used in agriculture to produce clones from a fertilised egg. This isn't how the famous Dolly the sheep was produced, by the way.

a) By what process does the fertilised egg divide?

b) Why are the two offspring produced called clones?

c) **i)** What are the advantages of using this technique?
ii) What are the disadvantages of using this technique?

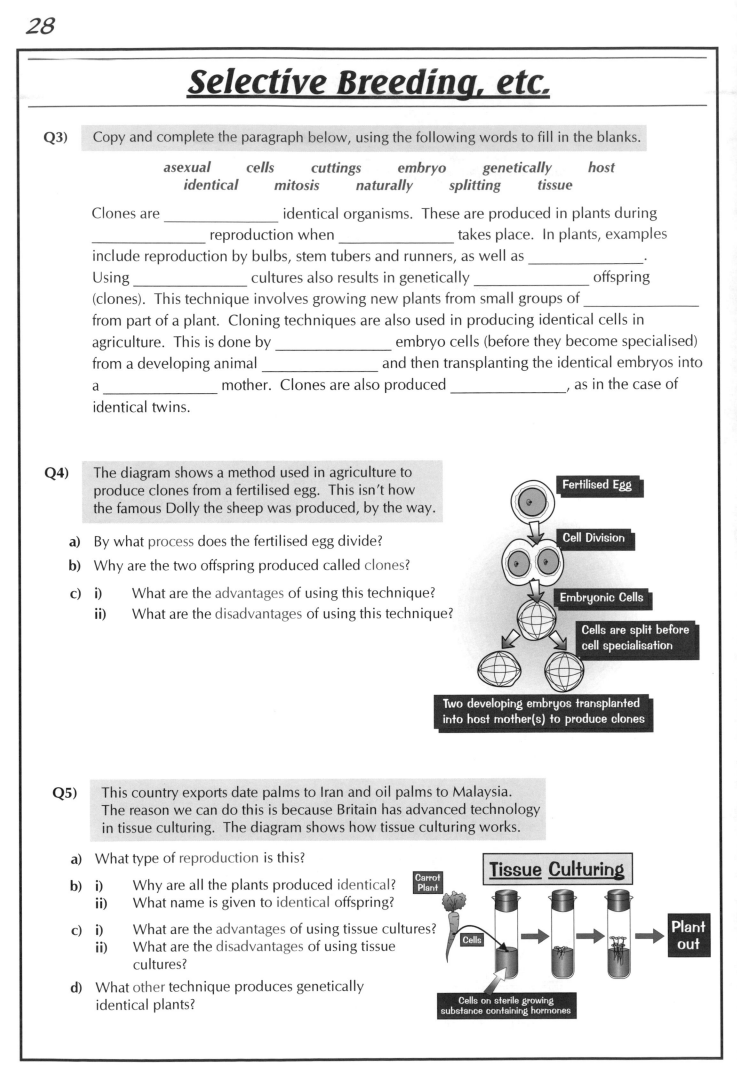

Q5) This country exports date palms to Iran and oil palms to Malaysia.
The reason we can do this is because Britain has advanced technology in tissue culturing. The diagram shows how tissue culturing works.

a) What type of reproduction is this?

b) **i)** Why are all the plants produced identical?
ii) What name is given to identical offspring?

c) **i)** What are the advantages of using tissue cultures?
ii) What are the disadvantages of using tissue cultures?

d) What other technique produces genetically identical plants?

Population Sizes

Q1) There are twelve sycamore trees in a wood. Their environment is quite sunny, with plenty of nutrients in the soil. They share the wood with many other plants and animals.

a) What is the population of sycamore trees in the wood?

b) What is the habitat of the sycamore trees?

c) Match the terms to the correct definitions:

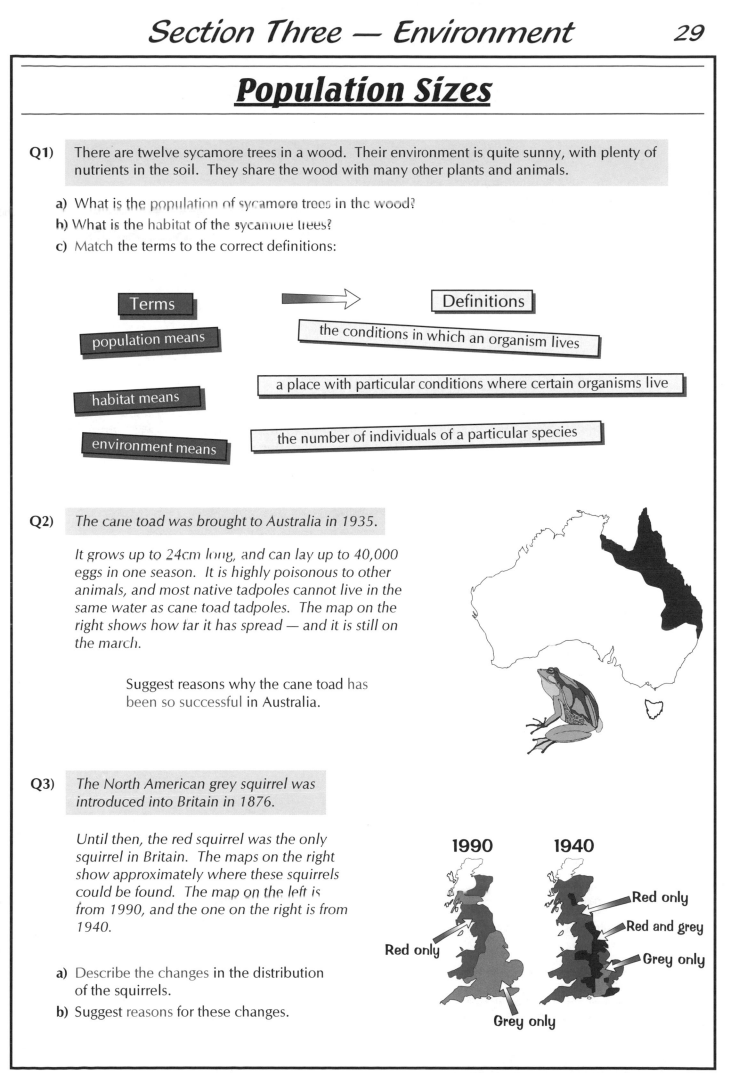

Terms

population means

habitat means

environment means

Definitions

the conditions in which an organism lives

a place with particular conditions where certain organisms live

the number of individuals of a particular species

Q2) *The cane toad was brought to Australia in 1935.*

It grows up to 24cm long, and can lay up to 40,000 eggs in one season. It is highly poisonous to other animals, and most native tadpoles cannot live in the same water as cane toad tadpoles. The map on the right shows how far it has spread — and it is still on the march.

Suggest reasons why the cane toad has been so successful in Australia.

Q3) *The North American grey squirrel was introduced into Britain in 1876.*

Until then, the red squirrel was the only squirrel in Britain. The maps on the right show approximately where these squirrels could be found. The map on the left is from 1990, and the one on the right is from 1940.

1990   1940

Red only

Red and grey

Grey only

Red only

Grey only

a) Describe the changes in the distribution of the squirrels.

b) Suggest reasons for these changes.

Adapt and Survive

Q1) Many desert animals, such as the kangaroo rat, spend the day in a burrow and come out at night.

What are the advantages and disadvantages of doing this?

Q2) Camels are probably the best-known animals in the desert.

There are two types, the Bactrian camel (right) and the
Arabian camel or dromedary (left).

a) Describe the features that the camels have in common which
make them adapted for desert conditions.

b) It has been discovered that a camel without hair loses nearly twice as much body water as a
normal camel. Suggest why losing its hair could cause this difference.

c) Humans need to maintain a fairly constant body temperature, but camels can tolerate a big
change in their body temperature. They can allow it to go from about 34°C to 41°C during the day,
and then they cool off during the night. This means that during the day they do not need to use
methods of cooling that humans do. How is this advantageous to the camel?

Q3) Lemmings are small rodents that live in the tundra.

They have a rounded body about 12cm long. Their fur is light brown, and
they have small ears that are hidden by fur. Lemmings live in burrows.
Explain how the lemming is adapted to life in the Arctic.

Q4) Polar bears and walruses are probably the best known
animals in the Arctic. Both have large bodies, with thick
layers of fat under the skin. The polar bear has fur that
looks white in the light. The walrus has long tusks and
tough brown skin. Male walruses often fight each other.

a) Suggest why polar bears and walruses do not live in burrows.

b) Explain how polar bears and walruses are adapted to life in the Arctic.

Q5) The snowshoe hare has white fur in the winter and reddish-brown fur in the summer.

Suggest a reason for this change.

Q6) Desert foxes have very large ears, whereas Arctic foxes only have very small ears.

Suggest a reason for this difference (it is not to do with hearing or hiding).

Top Tips Obviously, animals and plants <u>not</u> suited to the environment will be <u>less likely</u> to
survive than those which <u>are</u>. By <u>natural selection</u> creatures have evolved <u>features</u> that help them to
cope. The camel and polar bear examples are good ones to remember because the features are <u>shared</u>
by lots of other animals in <u>similar environments</u>.

Problems Caused By Farming

Q1) Answer these questions about pesticides:

a) What is a pesticide? Give an example of a pesticide. Why are pesticides useful to farmers?

b) In a study of an aquatic food chain in a small pond, it was found that many of the animals contained a fat-soluble pesticide called Kilzemall. The results are shown below.
Describe and explain the trend in the concentration of Kilzemall going up the food chain.

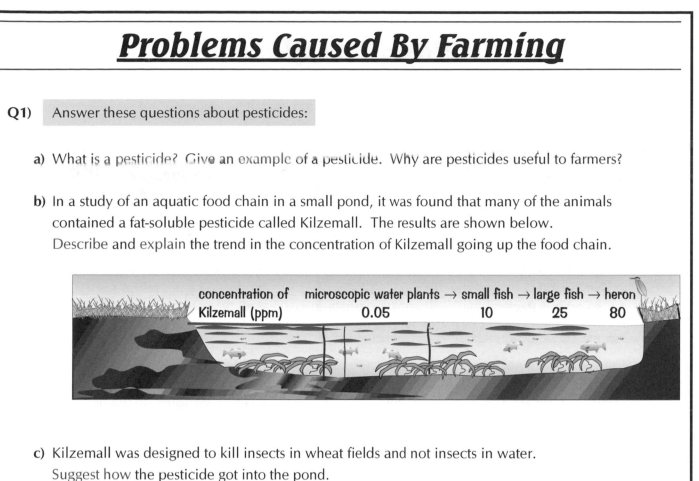

concentration of Kilzemall (ppm)	microscopic water plants →	small fish →	large fish →	heron
	0.05	10	25	80

c) Kilzemall was designed to kill insects in wheat fields and not insects in water.
Suggest how the pesticide got into the pond.

d) In later studies, scientists were astonished to discover that polar bears and penguins contained high amounts of Kilzemall in their bodies. Suggest how the pesticide managed to get into their bodies. Remember: polar bears and penguins only meet in zoos, and farmers are not likely to be doing any farming at the poles.

e) Modern pesticides are tested in many ways to ensure their safety.
Explain why we should be concerned about the health of organisms exposed to pesticides.

Q2) More use of machinery (mechanisation) has caused the average size of fields and farms to increase greatly. This has been achieved by felling trees and removing hedges between smaller fields.

a) Why are larger fields needed for machinery such as combine harvesters, tractors and ploughs?

b) What problems are caused to wildlife communities when trees and hedges are removed?

Managed Ecosystems

Q1) The sentences below are steps in a lake becoming eutrophic, but they are muddled up.

    a) Sort them into the correct order and write them down.

- Fish and other aquatic animals die of suffocation.
- The microbes take more oxygen from the water for their respiration.
- Excess fertilisers leach from the soil and are washed into the lake.
- The number of microbes that feed on dead organisms increases.
- There is increased competition between the plants, and some die as a result.
- Water plants in the lake start to grow rapidly.

b) In the corrected sequence, why should water plants grow more quickly?

c) What resources are the water plants competing for? Which resource is probably in excess?

d) If there are more plants in the lake, you might expect more oxygen to be produced by photosynthesis. Why does the oxygen content of the water go down instead?

Normally, the action of decomposers such as bacteria is welcomed because it allows scarce nutrients to be recycled for use by other organisms in the community, as in the nitrogen cycle.

    e) Why is the action of decomposers such a problem in the case of a eutrophic lake?

    f) Describe some environmental and economic consequences of eutrophication.

    g) Suggest two courses of action that might be taken to rescue a lake which is becoming eutrophic.

Q2) In the UK, fish is a very popular food. If we carry on eating so much fish, however, we could run the risk of making many fish species endangered. This is why fish farming has been introduced — to rear fish in a deliberately controlled way.

Copy and complete the sentences below using the words in the box.

pollution	reproduction	energy	pesticides	predators	disease

On a fish farm, fish are kept in cages to protect them from .... and to stop them from using so much .... in swimming. Their diet is carefully controlled to avoid .... to the lake. Their .... is also controlled as eggs are artificially fertilised and the young are reared in special tanks to make as many survive as possible. A disadvantage of fish farming is that the fish are more prone to .... and parasites. Chemical .... can be used to treat this problem, but they can harm other creatures in the lake. A better solution would be to use biological pest control if possible.

Q3) Traditional farming methods produce less food per acre than modern methods, and they are more expensive. As a result, we barely use traditional methods any more — and we are over-producing food.

    a) Name the main advantage of traditional farming methods over modern ones.

    b) Suggest two things that can be done to help achieve this advantage whilst still allowing us to produce plenty of food.

There's Too Many People

Q1) Copy and complete these examples of how the environment has been damaged by the abuse (the over-use) of the Earth's resources.

a) The growing world population has led to increasing demands for f.......... and w..................

b) The over-use of the farmland leads to s.............. e................ and des..........................

c) The ruthless demands for timber have led to de............................... and f.......................

d) Mining and quarrying damage hab................. and create eye.................

Q2) Choose the correct word from the brackets to complete the sentences.

a) The (increasing / decreasing) standard of living in many countries demands more from the environment.

b) We are rapidly using up our supplies of (renewable / non-renewable) energy resources which exerts more pressure on the environment.

c) The increase in the population of the world means that (more / less) waste is produced.

d) When there were fewer people in the world, the effects of human activity were more (local / global).

e) Farming and building have caused (increases / decreases) in the amount of land available for wild plants and animals.

Q3) The activity of humans can pollute all three parts of the environment.

Match the parts of the environment to its pollutants.

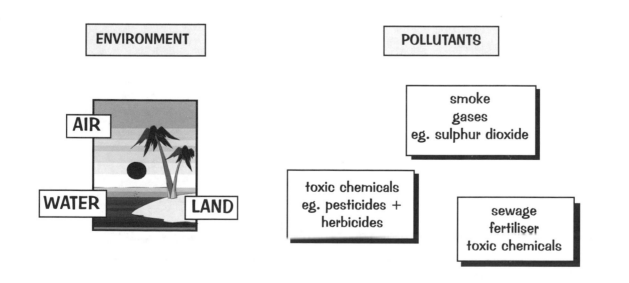

ENVIRONMENT

AIR

WATER LAND

POLLUTANTS

smoke
gases
eg. sulphur dioxide

toxic chemicals
eg. pesticides +
herbicides

sewage
fertiliser
toxic chemicals

Top Tips This is a really important subject — not just for your exams but also for the future of the Earth. Wow. Just remember, the world's population is <u>rising out of control</u> and this is putting pressure on the environment in three ways — through the demand for better <u>living conditions</u>, the reduction of <u>land available</u>, and general <u>environmental damage</u>.

Section Three — Environment

Air Pollution and The Greenhouse Effect

Q1) The table on the left shows the amount of acid rain gases from different sources.

The percentage contributions of nitrogen oxides have been plotted on the graph below.

Acid Rain Gas	Source	%
Sulphur dioxide	Industry	10
	Other	8
	Domestic	5
	Power stations	34
Nitrogen oxides	Road transport	22
	Power stations	13
	Other	5
	Industry	4

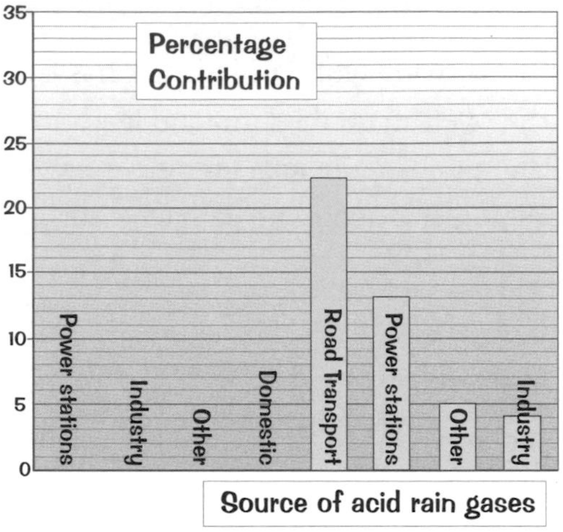

a) Copy and complete the graph to show the percentage contributions of sulphur dioxide from the different sources.

b) Which source produces the most sulphur dioxide?

c) Which source produces the most nitrogen oxides?

d) Which source produces the most acid rain gases overall?

Q2) The temperature on the surface of the Moon ranges from -175°C to 125°C. The average temperature on the surface of the Moon is about -20°C.

The differences between the Moon's surface temperature and the Earth's surface temperature are mainly because the Earth has an atmosphere.
Our atmosphere traps heat by a process known as the greenhouse effect.

Copy and complete the diagram below to show how the greenhouse effect works.

Choose from these labels:

Earth's surface
Earth's atmosphere
Heat from the Sun
Heat absorbed by the atmosphere

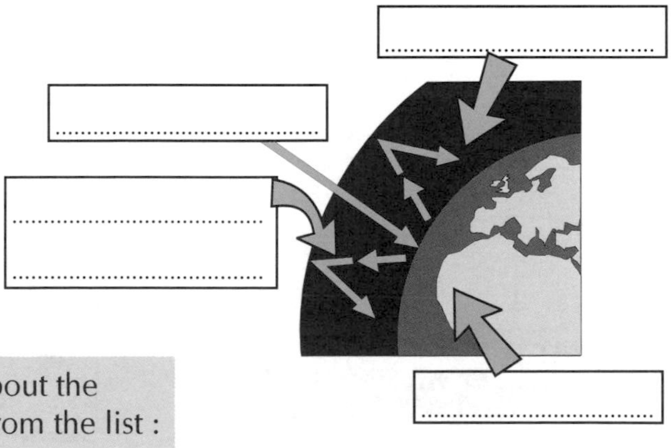

Q3) Copy and complete the paragraph below about the greenhouse effect using the correct words from the list :

good	absorbed	surface	Sun	atmosphere	space	warms

Energy from the .... passes through the Earth's .... and warms the Earth's surface. Heat energy from the Earth's .... is radiated into ...., but some of it is .... by gases in the atmosphere. This .... the atmosphere, which is .... for life on Earth.

Air Pollution and The Greenhouse Effect

Q4) Only some of the gases in the atmosphere, called greenhouse gases, are good at absorbing heat energy. These include carbon dioxide and methane, which both occur naturally in the atmosphere.

a) Name a natural source of carbon dioxide.

b) Since the Industrial Revolution began in the 19th century, humans have been burning more fossil fuels. Name a greenhouse gas released by burning fossil fuels.

c) Study the top graph on the right, which shows the amount of carbon released from burning fossil fuel since 1850. Describe the graph — how has the release of carbon from fossil fuels changed?

Suggest why this change happened.

d) Study the bottom graph on the right, which shows the amount of carbon dioxide in the atmosphere since 1850. Describe the graph — how has the amount of carbon dioxide in the atmosphere changed?

Suggest why this change happened.

e) There are natural processes that can absorb the carbon released as carbon dioxide from fossil fuels.

Name one of these processes.

f) Explain what the changes in the amount of carbon dioxide in the atmosphere could do to the temperature of the Earth.

g) Suggest how changes in the Earth's temperature ("global warming") could cause a change in sea level.

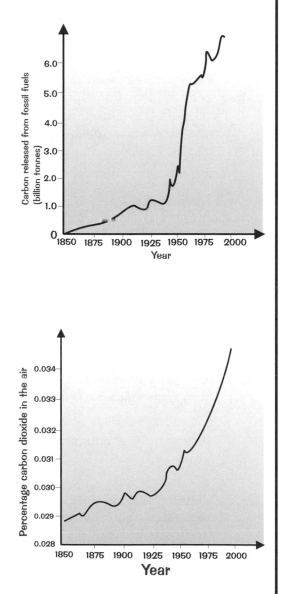

Top Tips   You've got to understand the **factors** that lead to increased greenhouse effect and global warming. The greenhouse effect is good for life on Earth because it keeps us nice and warm, but getting **too** warm will muck up the **climate** and melt the **ice caps**.

Section Three — Environment

Acid Rain

Q1) Answer these questions about the formation of acid rain:

a) What gases dissolve in clouds to make acid rain?

b) What acids can be found in acid rain?

Q2) Acid rain can react with limestone and marble statues and stonework on buildings, causing them to be eroded. For a long time, it was not clear that acid rain was damaging trees. The map on the right shows how much damage has been done to trees in Europe.

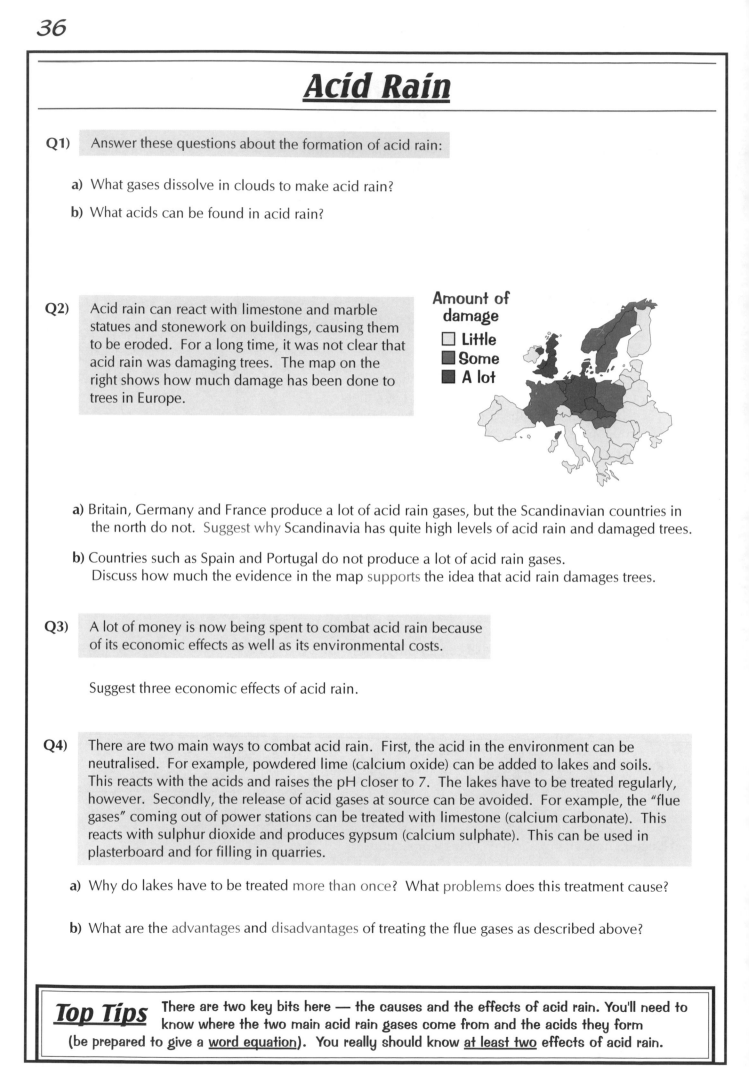

Amount of damage
☐ Little
▨ Some
■ A lot

a) Britain, Germany and France produce a lot of acid rain gases, but the Scandinavian countries in the north do not. Suggest why Scandinavia has quite high levels of acid rain and damaged trees.

b) Countries such as Spain and Portugal do not produce a lot of acid rain gases. Discuss how much the evidence in the map supports the idea that acid rain damages trees.

Q3) A lot of money is now being spent to combat acid rain because of its economic effects as well as its environmental costs.

Suggest three economic effects of acid rain.

Q4) There are two main ways to combat acid rain. First, the acid in the environment can be neutralised. For example, powdered lime (calcium oxide) can be added to lakes and soils. This reacts with the acids and raises the pH closer to 7. The lakes have to be treated regularly, however. Secondly, the release of acid gases at source can be avoided. For example, the "flue gases" coming out of power stations can be treated with limestone (calcium carbonate). This reacts with sulphur dioxide and produces gypsum (calcium sulphate). This can be used in plasterboard and for filling in quarries.

a) Why do lakes have to be treated more than once? What problems does this treatment cause?

b) What are the advantages and disadvantages of treating the flue gases as described above?

Top Tips There are two key bits here — the causes and the effects of acid rain. You'll need to know where the two main acid rain gases come from and the acids they form (be prepared to give a _word equation_). You really should know _at least two_ effects of acid rain.

Section Three — Environment

Atoms

Q1   Answer these questions on atoms:

a) What is an atom?

b) How many different subatomic particles make up an atom?

c) What are their names?

d) What is a nucleus?

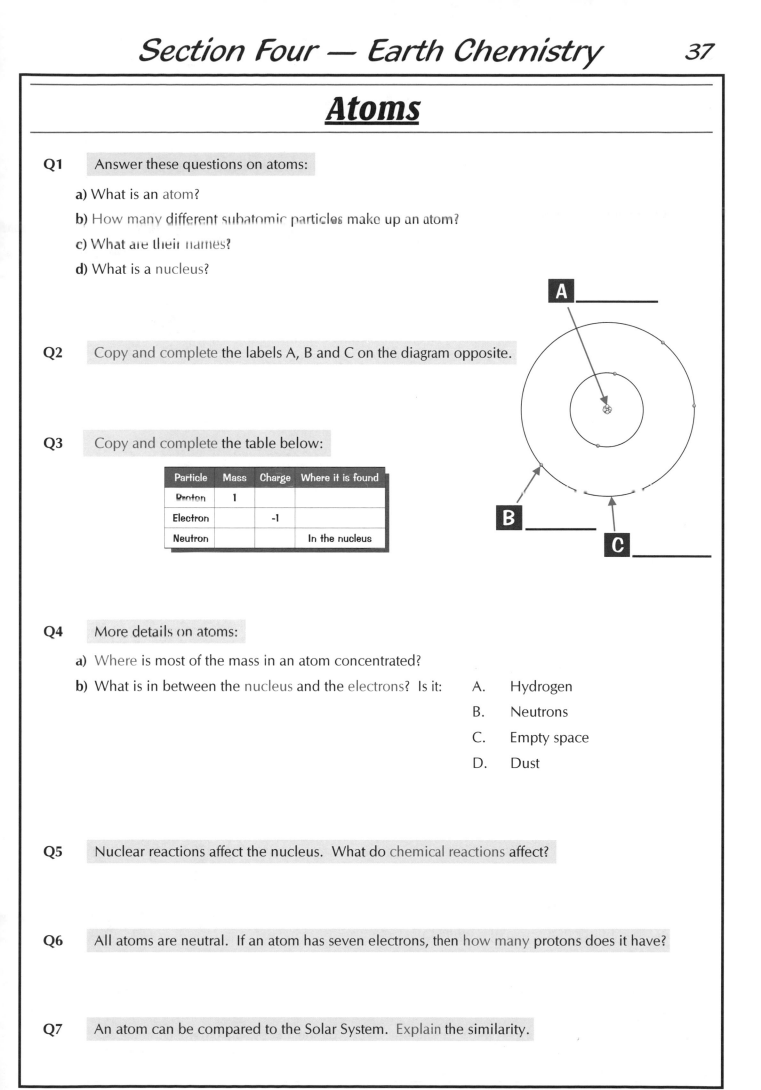

Q2   Copy and complete the labels A, B and C on the diagram opposite.

Q3   Copy and complete the table below:

Particle	Mass	Charge	Where it is found
Proton	1		
Electron		-1	
Neutron			In the nucleus

Q4   More details on atoms:

a) Where is most of the mass in an atom concentrated?

b) What is in between the nucleus and the electrons? Is it:

A.   Hydrogen

B.   Neutrons

C.   Empty space

D.   Dust

Q5   Nuclear reactions affect the nucleus. What do chemical reactions affect?

Q6   All atoms are neutral. If an atom has seven electrons, then how many protons does it have?

Q7   An atom can be compared to the Solar System. Explain the similarity.

Atoms

Q8 Answer these questions on the atomic number and mass number of an element:

a) What does the atomic number tell us?

b) What does the mass number tell us?

c) What do the letters A and Z in the diagram stand for? What is A – Z?

d) How many protons are there in an atom of lithium?

e) How many electrons are there in an atom of lithium?

f) How many neutrons are there in an atom of lithium?

g) Which number (mass or atomic) determines what element an atom is?

$$^7_3\text{Li}$$

A → 7

Z → 3

Q9 Copy and complete the table below:

Element	Number of protons	Number of electrons	Number of neutrons
a) Carbon $^{12}_{6}\text{C}$			
b) Magnesium $^{24}_{12}\text{Mg}$			
c) Potassium $^{39}_{19}\text{K}$			
d) Hydrogen $^{1}_{1}\text{H}$			

Q10 What are isotopes?

Q11 Calculate the number of protons, electrons and neutrons in:

a) Deuterium (^2_1H)   b) Tritium (^3_1H)

Top Tips

Some tricky new terms here — that's Science for you. You must know the **difference** between __atomic number__ and __mass number__. Doing questions like this is excellent practice — come the Exam, it'll be easy marks. Bet you can't wait...

Electron Shells and Ionic Bonding

Q1   Copy and complete the table to show the sizes of the electron shells:

Electron shell	Maximum number of electrons in the shell
1st	
2nd	

Q2   What is an ion?

Q3   Copy and complete this paragraph using the words provided:

–ve   protons   negatively charged   neutral   positively charged

Atoms are electrically _____ because they have equal numbers of _____ (+ve) and
electrons (_____). If electrons are taken away from a metal atom or hydrogen, then it
becomes _____ because it has fewer electrons than protons. If electrons are added
to a non-metal atom, it becomes _____ because it then has more electrons than protons.

Q4   Draw out the ions below exactly like the examples below Q5.

(Remember Group 1 make 1$^+$ ions and Group 2 make 2$^+$.)
  a) Potassium   **b)** Magnesium   **c)** Calcium   **d)** Aluminium

Q5   Draw out the ions below exactly like those below.

(Remember Group 7 make 1$^-$ ions and Group 6 make 2$^-$).
   a) Fluoride   **b)** Chloride   **c)** Sulphide   **d)** Oxide

---

Example 1: Positive Ions (metals and hydrogen)

$^{23}_{11}$Na

Loses one electron

SODIUM ION FROM SODIUM

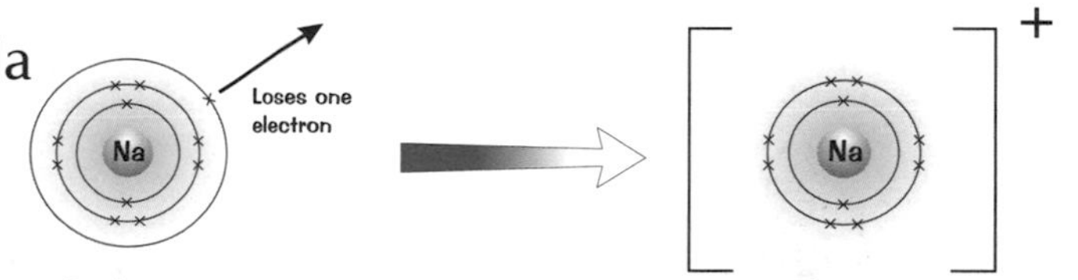

Na — Sodium atoms: 2, 8, 1

Na$^+$ — Sodium ion: 2, 8

Example 2: Negative Ions (non-metals)

$^{16}_{8}$O

Gains two electrons

OXIDE ION FROM OXYGEN

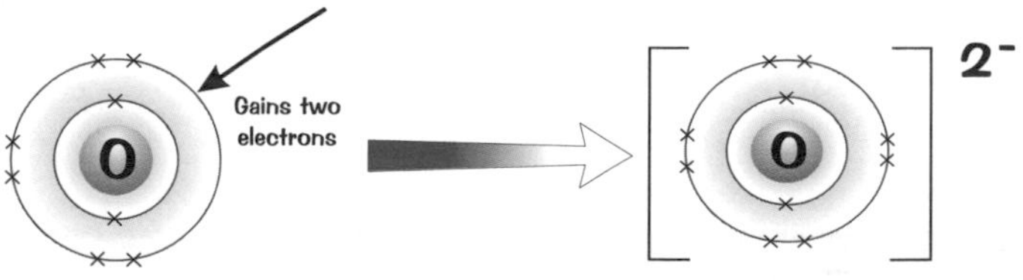

O — Oxygen atoms: 2, 6

O^{2-} — Oxide ion: Oxide: 2, 8

Common Tests and Hazard Symbols

Q1 Match each substance with the correct lab test:

a) Chlorine	turns limewater milky
b) Oxygen	bleaches damp litmus paper
c) Carbon dioxide	has a boiling point of 100°C
d) Hydrogen	burns with a squeaky pop
e) Water	relights a glowing splint

Q2 Link up the hazchem symbols with their description, and give an example of each:

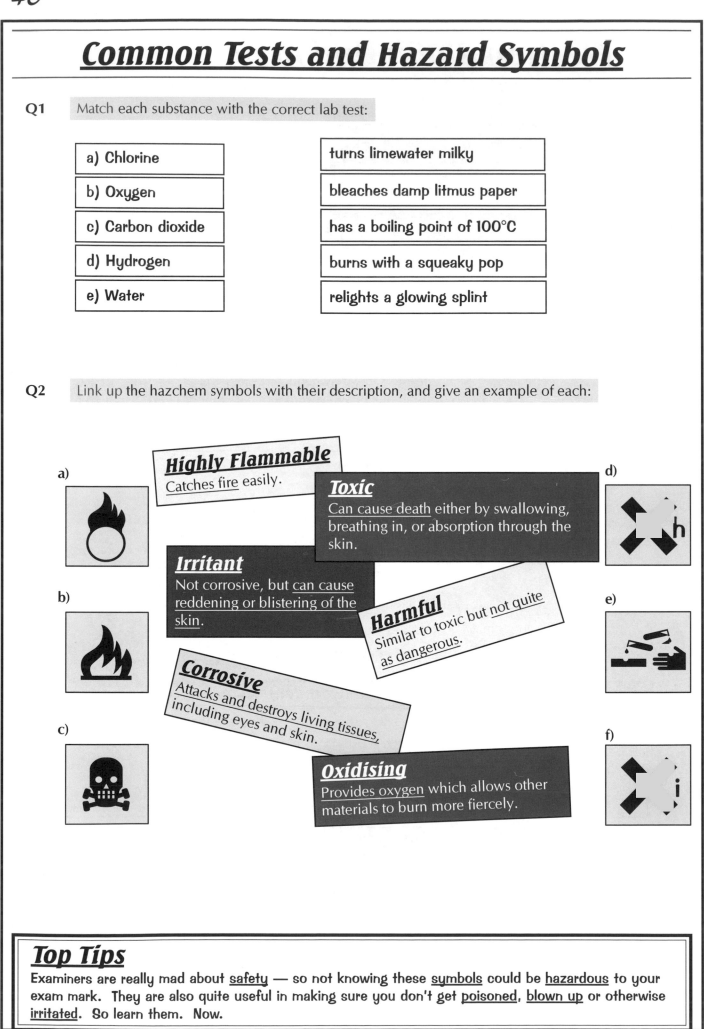

a)

Highly Flammable
Catches fire easily.

Toxic
Can cause death either by swallowing, breathing in, or absorption through the skin.

d)

Irritant
Not corrosive, but can cause reddening or blistering of the skin.

b)

Harmful
Similar to toxic but not quite as dangerous.

e)

Corrosive
Attacks and destroys living tissues, including eyes and skin.

c)

Oxidising
Provides oxygen which allows other materials to burn more fiercely.

f)

Top Tips
Examiners are really mad about <u>safety</u> — so not knowing these <u>symbols</u> could be <u>hazardous</u> to your exam mark. They are also quite useful in making sure you don't get <u>poisoned</u>, <u>blown up</u> or otherwise <u>irritated</u>. So learn them. Now.

Fractional Distillation of Crude Oil

Q1   Explain in your own words how crude oil is formed.

Q2   Crude oil is a mixture of what?

Q3   What is a hydrocarbon? Give an example of a hydrocarbon.

Q4   What is a fossil fuel?

Q5   Write down the fractions represented by the labels A to E below.

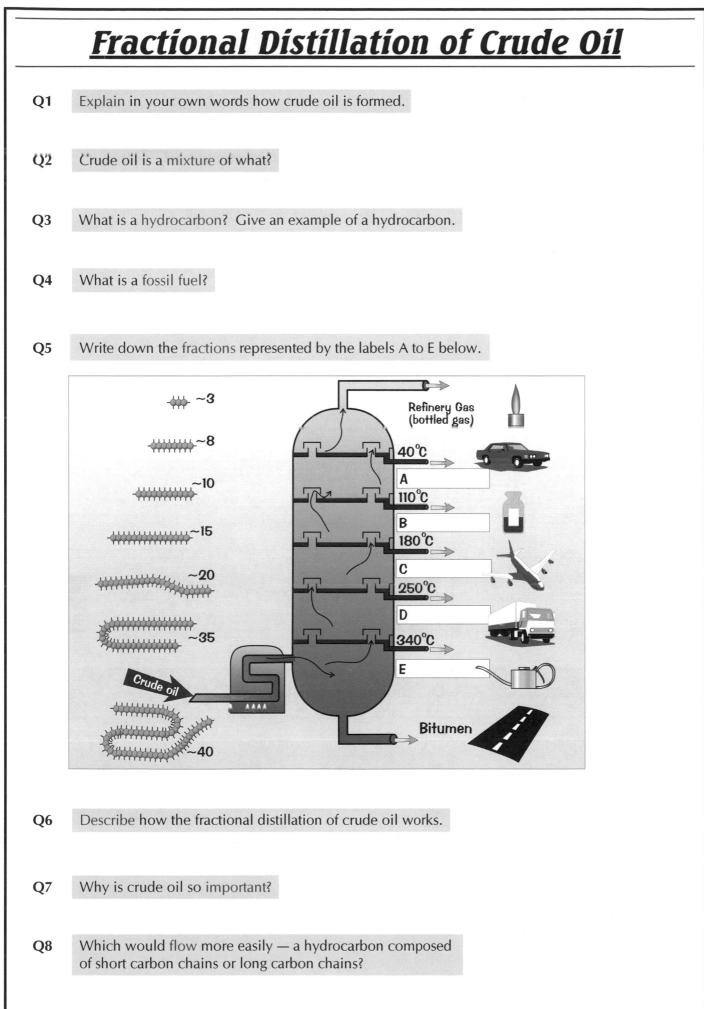

Q6   Describe how the fractional distillation of crude oil works.

Q7   Why is crude oil so important?

Q8   Which would flow more easily — a hydrocarbon composed
of short carbon chains or long carbon chains?

Section Four — Earth Chemistry

Using Hydrocarbons

Q1   How does the boiling point of a hydrocarbon change as its carbon chain length increases?

Q2   How does the flammability of a hydrocarbon change as its carbon chain length increases?

Q3   How does the volatility of a hydrocarbon change as its carbon chain length increases?

Q4   Which fractions will ignite most easily — short carbon chains or long carbon chains?

Q5   Why is it dangerous to burn alkanes in a limited oxygen supply?

Q6   Copy and complete the paragraph using the words below:

	blue	water	carbon dioxide
carbon monoxide	yellow	incomplete	

The complete combustion of hydrocarbons in oxygen will produce only

_____ _____ and _____. If there is plenty of

oxygen the gas burns with a clean _____ flame.

If there isn't enough oxygen the combustion will be _____

and the gas will burn with a smoky _____ flame. The poisonous gas

_____ _____ is one of the products and is very dangerous.

Cracking Hydrocarbons

H Q1   What is cracking?

H Q2   Give two reasons why it is carried out.

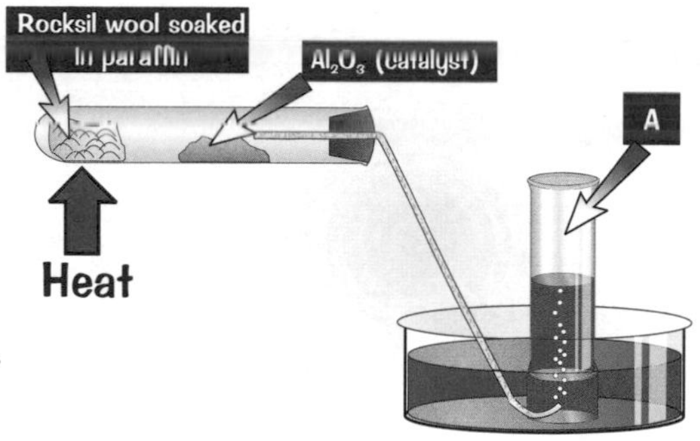

Rocksil wool soaked in paraffin

Al_2O_3 (catalyst)

A

Heat

H Q3   Look at the diagram to the right.

a) Name two conditions that are needed to crack paraffin.

b) Gas A produced in this reaction is an alkene.
What is an alkene?

c) Alkenes are unsaturated. What does this mean?

d) Paraffin does not decolourise orange/brown bromine water,
but gas "A" collected in the gas jar does. Explain these observations.

H Q4   Only the larger fractions obtained by the distillation of crude oil are cracked. Why is this?

H Q5 $C_{16}H_{34}$ was heated strongly with a catalyst, in the absence of air.
This is one reaction that occurred:

$$C_{16}H_{34} \rightarrow 2C_2H_4 + C_6H_{12} + C_6H_{14}$$

a) Name the process shown in the equation.

b) Which of these molecules are unsaturated?

c) Which of them are saturated?

d) Which molecules would:
    i) Decolourise bromine water?
    ii) Polymerise?

e) Name two uses of "cracked" hydrocarbons.

Top Tips

We break up long hydrocarbons to make them <u>less viscous</u>, and more importantly to produce <u>alkenes</u>.
If you take a long hydrocarbon, and make a shorter one out of it, the bit left over <u>has</u> to be an alkene,
cos otherwise there aren't enough bonds to go round. Remember alkenes have a C=C <u>double bond</u>,
and they join up to make <u>polymers</u> — cracking stuff.

Alkanes and Alkenes

H Q1 Copy and complete the table by filling in the missing information:

Alkanes = C_nH_{2n+2}

Name	Formula	Number of Carbons	Structural Formula
Methane	CH_4	1	H‑C‑H (with H above and below)
Ethane	C_2H_6		H‑C‑C‑H (with H's)
Propane	C_3H_8	3	
Butane		4	H‑C‑C‑C‑C‑H (with H's)

Alkanes are organic compounds that form a homologous series of hydrocarbons. They only contain single covalent bonds and are therefore saturated hydrocarbons. They form 3D molecules but are usually drawn flat. They have the general formula C_nH_{2n+2}. They do not decolourise bromine water and they burn cleanly to produce carbon dioxide and water.

H Q2 Explain what is meant by a "single covalent bond".

H Q3 Explain why alkanes do not react with bromine water.

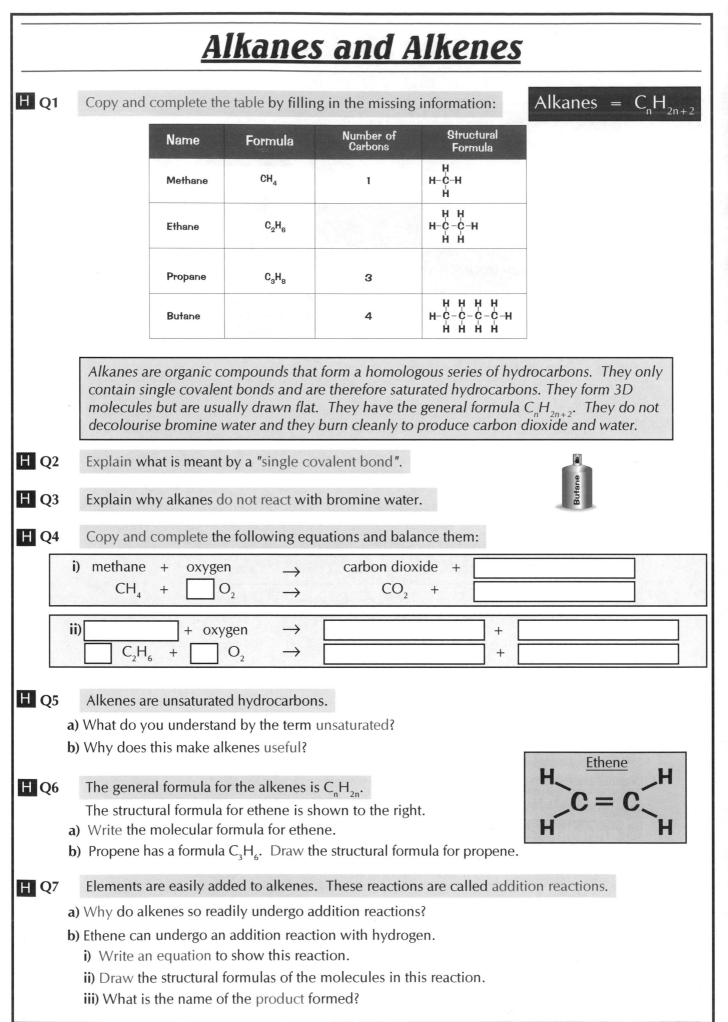

H Q4 Copy and complete the following equations and balance them:

i) methane + oxygen → carbon dioxide + [   ]

CH_4 + [ ] O_2 → CO_2 + [   ]

ii) [   ] + oxygen → [   ] + [   ]

[ ] C_2H_6 + [ ] O_2 → [   ] + [   ]

H Q5 Alkenes are unsaturated hydrocarbons.

a) What do you understand by the term unsaturated?

b) Why does this make alkenes useful?

H Q6 The general formula for the alkenes is C_nH_{2n}.

The structural formula for ethene is shown to the right.

a) Write the molecular formula for ethene.

b) Propene has a formula C_3H_6. Draw the structural formula for propene.

Ethene

$$H{-}C{=}C{-}H$$ (with H's)

H Q7 Elements are easily added to alkenes. These reactions are called addition reactions.

a) Why do alkenes so readily undergo addition reactions?

b) Ethene can undergo an addition reaction with hydrogen.

i) Write an equation to show this reaction.

ii) Draw the structural formulas of the molecules in this reaction.

iii) What is the name of the product formed?

Polymers and Plastics

H Q1   Explain what you understand by the term "polymerisation".

H Q2   Ethene can undergo many addition reactions to form long chain polymers.

What reaction conditions are necessary for this to happen?

H Q3   Lots of ethene molecules can join together to form a substance that is useful.

a) Using the ethene molecule to help you, draw a diagram to show how the monomers of ethene form their polymer.

b) What is this polymer called?

c) Explain the naming of ethene's polymer.

H Q4   Other alkenes can also break their double bond to form long chain polymers.

Copy the table below, then for each monomer given, draw what you would expect its polymer to look like, then name the polymer.

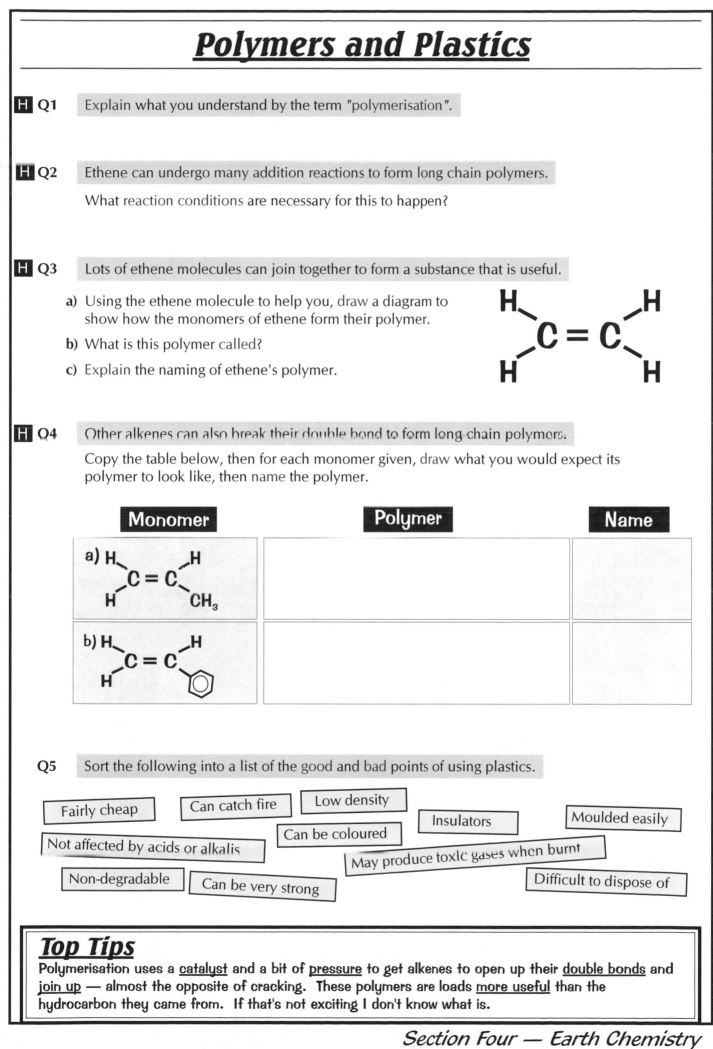

Monomer	Polymer	Name
a)		
b)		

Q5   Sort the following into a list of the good and bad points of using plastics.

Fairly cheap   Can catch fire   Low density   Insulators   Moulded easily

Can be coloured

Not affected by acids or alkalis

May produce toxic gases when burnt

Non-degradable   Can be very strong   Difficult to dispose of

Top Tips
Polymerisation uses a <u>catalyst</u> and a bit of <u>pressure</u> to get alkenes to open up their <u>double bonds</u> and <u>join up</u> — almost the opposite of cracking. These polymers are loads <u>more useful</u> than the hydrocarbon they came from. If that's not exciting I don't know what is.

Metal Ores from the Ground

Q1 What is a metal ore?

Q2 Give an example of a metal ore.

Q3 The diagram below shows some of the processes involved in extracting a metal from its ore.

Match each picture **a) - f)** with the correct expression from the following box:

Pure metal	Carbon reduction	Earth containing ore dug from ground	Electrolysis
	Metal ore detected in ground	Waste earth removed to concentrate ore	

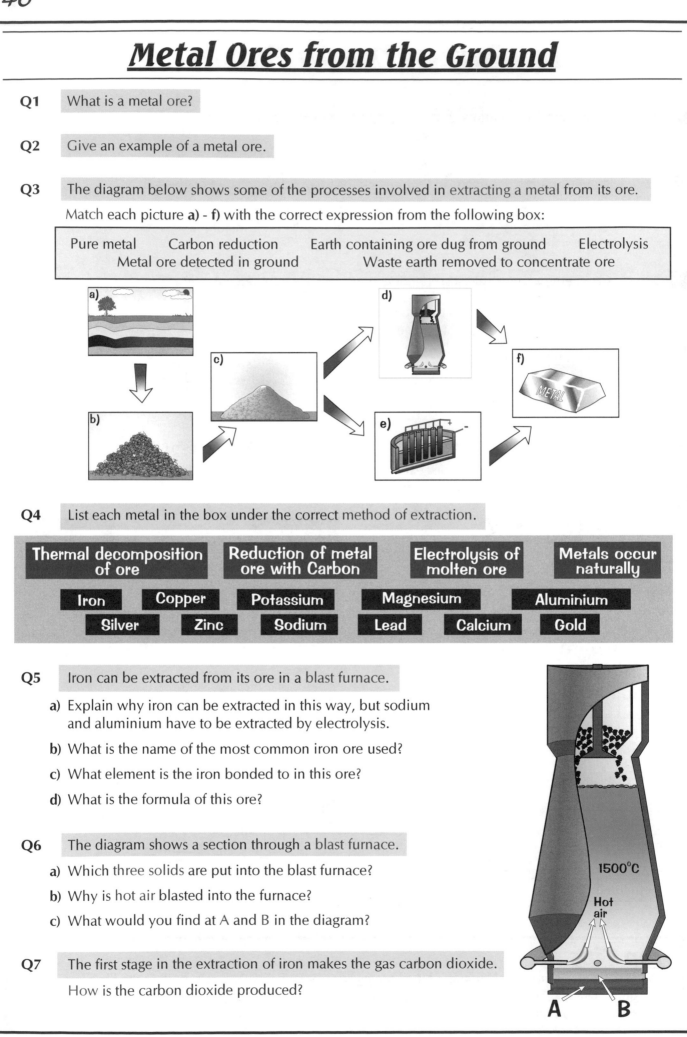

Q4 List each metal in the box under the correct method of extraction.

Thermal decomposition of ore	Reduction of metal ore with Carbon	Electrolysis of molten ore	Metals occur naturally

Iron   Copper   Potassium   Magnesium   Aluminium
Silver   Zinc   Sodium   Lead   Calcium   Gold

Q5 Iron can be extracted from its ore in a blast furnace.

a) Explain why iron can be extracted in this way, but sodium and aluminium have to be extracted by electrolysis.

b) What is the name of the most common iron ore used?

c) What element is the iron bonded to in this ore?

d) What is the formula of this ore?

Q6 The diagram shows a section through a blast furnace.

a) Which three solids are put into the blast furnace?

b) Why is hot air blasted into the furnace?

c) What would you find at A and B in the diagram?

Q7 The first stage in the extraction of iron makes the gas carbon dioxide.

How is the carbon dioxide produced?

1500°C

Hot air

A   B

Important Uses of Limestone

Answer these questions about limestone's formation and uses:

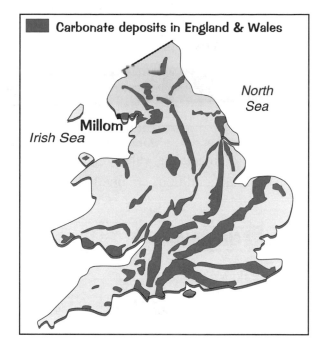

Carbonate deposits in England & Wales

North Sea

Millom

Irish Sea

Q1   What is the main substance in limestone?

Q2   What type of rock is it?

Q3   How has limestone formed?

Q4   When limestone is heated with sand and sodium carbonate it makes which important material?

Q5   What new material is formed when limestone is heated with clay?

Q6   The material in **Q5** can be mixed with sand and chippings.
Give the name of this mixture and a use for it.

Q7   Finely ground limestone is used to neutralise acidic soil. How does it neutralise the soil?

Q8   Calcium hydroxide forms when water is added to calcium oxide.
Give another name for calcium hydroxide.

Q9   Calcium hydroxide is also used to neutralise farm land.
What kind of substance is calcium hydroxide?

Top Tips

Limestone — not just any old lump of rock. You need to know that limestone is mainly <u>calcium carbonate</u> and that it is used to make handy stuff like <u>cement</u> and <u>glass</u>. And if that's not enough, you need to remember how it is made into <u>calcium oxide</u> and <u>calcium hydroxide</u> and what these are used for.

Using Ammonia to Make Fertilisers

Q1 Ammonia is made into fertilisers in three main stages.
Firstly, the ammonia needs to be converted into nitric acid.

Step 1 $NH_{3(g)} + 5O_{2(g)} \xrightarrow{Pt} 4NO_{(g)} + H_2O_{(l)}$

a) Balance this equation and state the products made in the reaction.

b) Ammonia reacts with oxygen as shown in the equation above.
What conditions are needed?

Step 2 $NO_{(g)} + 3O_{2\ (g)} + H_2O_{(g)} \rightarrow HNO_{3(aq)}$

c) Balance the equation.

d) Name the product formed in this reaction.

Step 3 Nitric acid then needs to be converted into ammonium nitrate.

e) What type of reaction is this?

f) Write a word equation and a balanced symbol equation for this reaction.

g) Ammonium nitrate is a fertiliser. Which element in ammonium nitrate is particularly useful for plants?

h) What do plants use this element for?

Q2 Nitrates are vital for plants. However, large quantities of nitrates in streams can cause algae and plants to grow out of control, which can eventually starve the stream, leading to death and decay.

a) What microbes are needed for decay to occur?

b) What element in the river does the decay process use up, and how will this affect the fish?

c) What is the name given to this whole process?

d) In your own words explain why nitrates cause the plants and algae to grow and why eventually this causes death.

e) How can farmers help to prevent all this happening?

The Periodic Table

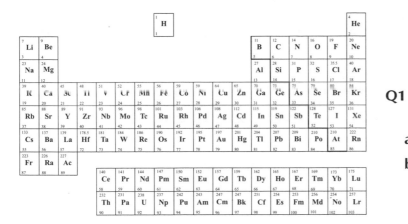

Q1 The Periodic Table is arranged in periods and groups.

a) What is meant by a group?

b) What is meant by a period?

Q2 All the known elements are listed in the Periodic Table.

a) Roughly how many elements are there?

b) In what order are the elements listed?

c) How is this different from the very first attempt at listing elements in a periodic table?

Q3 Elements in the same group share a number of different features.

a) Name one similarity between members of the same group.

b) Whose idea was it to put the elements in this order?

c) If an element is in Group I then how many electrons will it have in its outer electron shell?

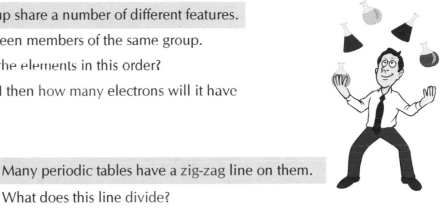

Q4 Many periodic tables have a zig-zag line on them.

a) What does this line divide?

b) Where are the metals in the Periodic Table in relation to this line?

c) Where are the non-metals in the Periodic Table in relation to this line?

Q5 One element is unlike any other as it is not a member of any group. Name this element.

Q6 Where are the transition metals found on the Periodic Table?

Q7 Members of Group III form 3+ ions. What ions do members of Group II form?

Q8 Sodium has an atomic number of 11 and a mass number of 23.
Explain in as much detail as possible what this tells us about an atom of sodium.

Top Tips
Remember that the <u>rows</u> are called <u>periods</u> and the vertical <u>columns</u> are called <u>groups</u>.
The groups "group" elements with similar properties. Make sure you can find your way around the
periodic table and know where your <u>metals</u>, <u>non-metals</u>, and <u>transition metals</u> are.

Electron Arrangements

Q1 Copy and complete the full electronic arrangement in the following dot and cross diagrams.

(The first three have been done for you.)

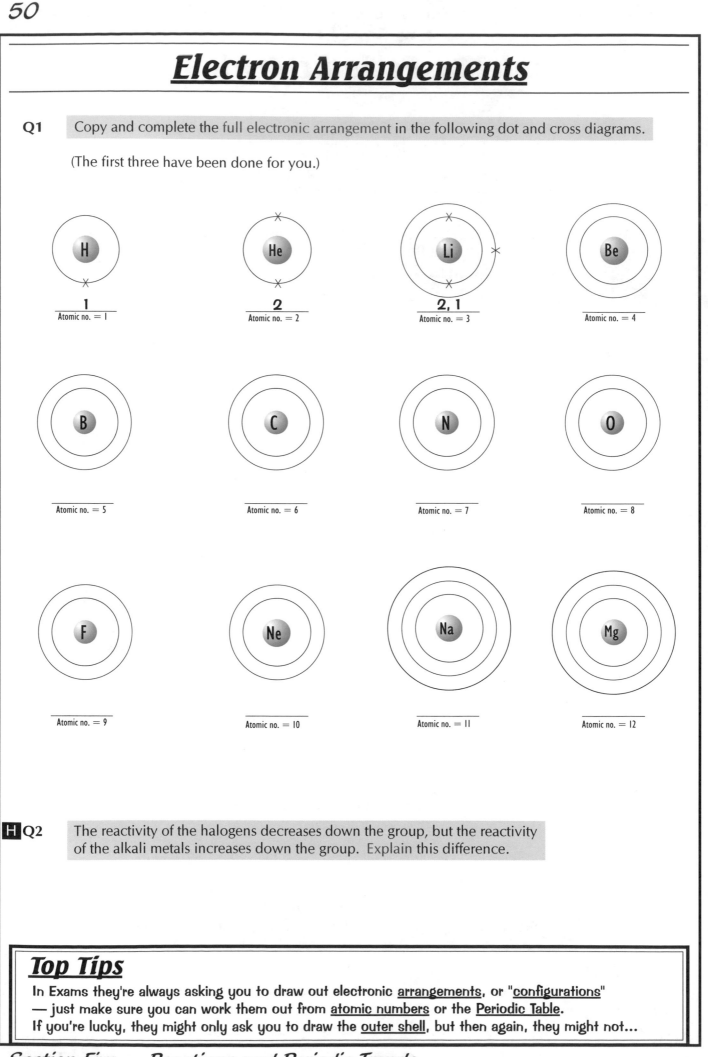

H Q2 The reactivity of the halogens decreases down the group, but the reactivity of the alkali metals increases down the group. Explain this difference.

Top Tips

In Exams they're always asking you to draw out electronic <u>arrangements</u>, or "<u>configurations</u>" — just make sure you can work them out from <u>atomic numbers</u> or the <u>Periodic Table</u>. If you're lucky, they might only ask you to draw the <u>outer shell</u>, but then again, they might not...

The Noble Gases and the Alkali Metals

Q1 Why are the noble gases sometimes known as Group VIII?

Q2 The noble gases are "inert". What does this mean?

Q3 By referring to their atomic structure, explain why the noble gases are inert.

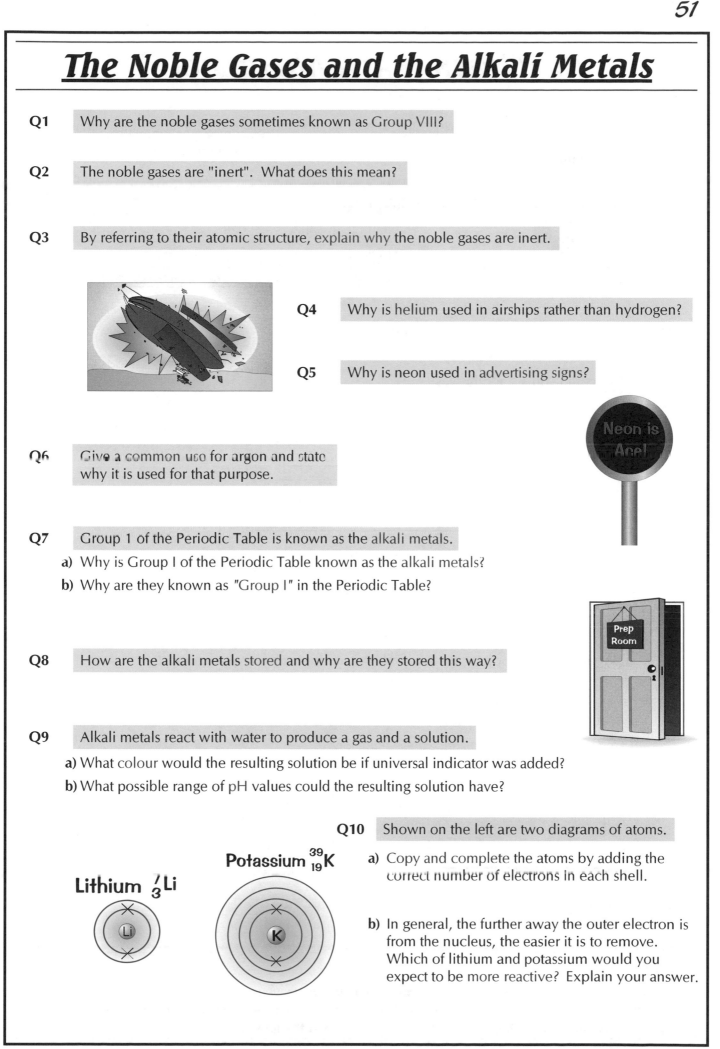

Q4 Why is helium used in airships rather than hydrogen?

Q5 Why is neon used in advertising signs?

Q6 Give a common use for argon and state why it is used for that purpose.

Q7 Group 1 of the Periodic Table is known as the alkali metals.

a) Why is Group I of the Periodic Table known as the alkali metals?

b) Why are they known as "Group I" in the Periodic Table?

Q8 How are the alkali metals stored and why are they stored this way?

Q9 Alkali metals react with water to produce a gas and a solution.

a) What colour would the resulting solution be if universal indicator was added?

b) What possible range of pH values could the resulting solution have?

Q10 Shown on the left are two diagrams of atoms.

Potassium $^{39}_{19}K$

Lithium $^{7}_{3}Li$

a) Copy and complete the atoms by adding the correct number of electrons in each shell.

b) In general, the further away the outer electron is from the nucleus, the easier it is to remove. Which of lithium and potassium would you expect to be more reactive? Explain your answer.

Reactions of the Alkali Metals

Q1 Put the metals in the box in order of reactivity — the most reactive first.

Caesium, Potassium, Lithium, Sodium, Rubidium.

Q2 Match up the alkali metal to its reaction in water:

A) Potassium

B) Sodium

C) Lithium

1) Ignites with yellow/orange flame, fizzes vigorously.

2) No flame, but fizzes.

3) Pops and ignites with a lilac flame, fizzes very vigorously.

Q3 When an alkali metal reacts with water, a gas is produced.

a) Name the gas that is produced.

b) How could you test for this gas?

c) Copy and complete the equations below.

Sodium + Water →

Lithium + Water →

d) i) Copy and complete and balance this equation:

$$K_{(s)} + H_2O_{(l)} \rightarrow KOH_{(aq)} + $$

ii) What do the symbols (s), (l), (aq), and (g) stand for in chemical equations?

Q4 Alkali metal oxides and hydroxides react with acids to form neutral salts.

Copy and complete and balance these equations:

$$NaOH + HCl \rightarrow + $$

$$Na_2O + 2HCl \rightarrow + $$

Q5 All alkali metal compounds dissolve easily in water. True or False?

Top Tips

With only <u>one</u> electron in their <u>outer shell</u>, these metals don't have much to lose — they're pretty <u>reactive</u>. The Exam's most likely to ask about <u>trends</u> in the group — make sure you know how <u>size</u>, <u>reactivity</u>, <u>density</u> and <u>melting</u> and <u>boiling points</u> vary down the group.

Group VII — The Halogens

Q1 Why are the halogens known as the Group VII elements?

Q2 Copy and complete the table below and answer the questions.

Halogen	Number of electrons in outer shell	State at room temperature	Colour at room temperature	Symbol
Fluorine	7			
Chlorine		gas		
Bromine			brown	
Iodine				I

a) Bromine is a brown volatile liquid. What is meant by volatile?

b) Why are the atoms bigger as you go down the group?

c) How does the reactivity change down the group?

Q3 Look at the information in the table.

a) From the information given, estimate the melting point of iodine.

b) Describe the patterns (trends) in the melting and boiling points down the group.

Halogen	Melting Point °C	Boiling Point °C
Fluorine	-220	-188
Chlorine	-101	-35
Bromine	-7	58
Iodine		184

Q4 Halogens react with metals to form salts.

a) Copy and complete the reactions shown on the right.

b) Are the salts ionic or covalent compounds? Explain your answer.

Iron + Chlorine →

Aluminium + Bromine →

Tin + Chlorine →

Q5 Chlorine is bubbled through sodium bromide as shown in the diagram.

a) What would you see happening in the test tube?

b) Which of chlorine or bromine is more reactive?

c) How can you explain the results of the reaction?

d) Write an equation to explain the reaction.

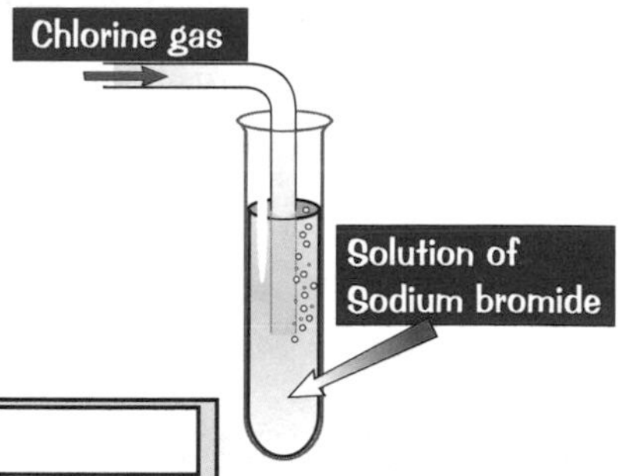

H e) Copy and complete the equations below but in balanced symbol form.

i) Fluorine + Sodium iodide →

ii) Chlorine + Sodium bromide →

iii) Chlorine + Potassium fluoride →

iv) Bromine + Potassium iodide →

Chlorine gas

Solution of Sodium bromide

Q6 Give two uses of chlorine.

Q7 Iodine is less reactive than fluorine, chlorine and bromine.

Name one use of iodine.

Acids and Alkalis

Q1   Copy and colour in the pH chart with the correct colours for Universal indicator solution:

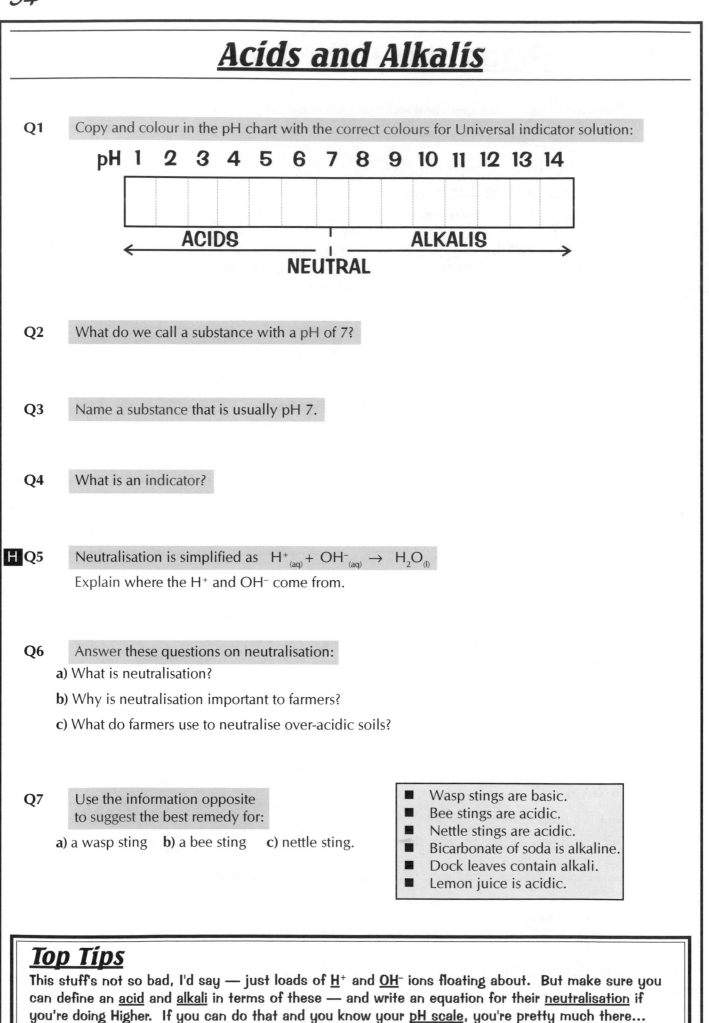

pH 1 2 3 4 5 6 7 8 9 10 11 12 13 14

←————— ACIDS ————— ————— ALKALIS —————→

NEUTRAL

Q2   What do we call a substance with a pH of 7?

Q3   Name a substance that is usually pH 7.

Q4   What is an indicator?

H Q5   Neutralisation is simplified as $H^+_{(aq)} + OH^-_{(aq)} \rightarrow H_2O_{(l)}$

Explain where the H^+ and OH^- come from.

Q6   Answer these questions on neutralisation:

a) What is neutralisation?

b) Why is neutralisation important to farmers?

c) What do farmers use to neutralise over-acidic soils?

Q7   Use the information opposite
to suggest the best remedy for:

a) a wasp sting   b) a bee sting   c) nettle sting.

- Wasp stings are basic.
- Bee stings are acidic.
- Nettle stings are acidic.
- Bicarbonate of soda is alkaline.
- Dock leaves contain alkali.
- Lemon juice is acidic.

Top Tips

This stuff's not so bad, I'd say — just loads of <u>H</u>+ and <u>OH</u>− ions floating about. But make sure you can define an <u>acid</u> and <u>alkali</u> in terms of these — and write an equation for their <u>neutralisation</u> if you're doing Higher. If you can do that and you know your <u>pH scale</u>, you're pretty much there...

Acids and Their Reactions

Q1 Copy and complete the following general reaction for a dilute acid.

> Acid + Metal → A Salt + _____

Q2 Why is it a bad idea to use sodium and hydrochloric acid to make sodium chloride?

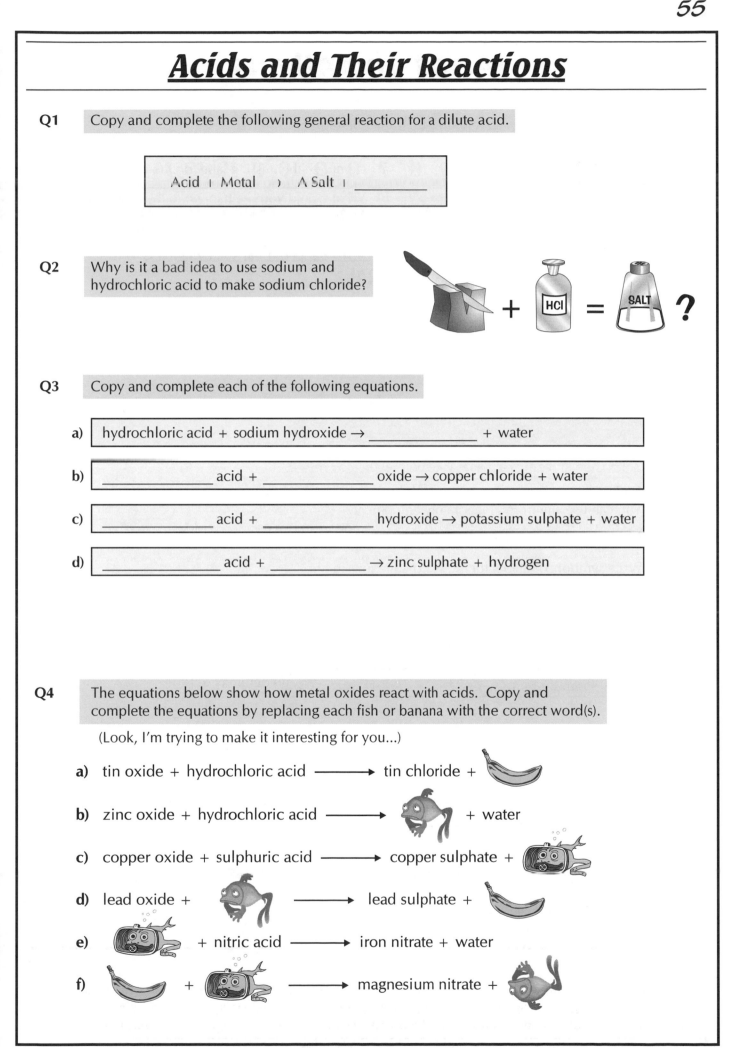

Q3 Copy and complete each of the following equations.

a) hydrochloric acid + sodium hydroxide → _____ + water

b) _____ acid + _____ oxide → copper chloride + water

c) _____ acid + _____ hydroxide → potassium sulphate + water

d) _____ acid + _____ → zinc sulphate + hydrogen

Q4 The equations below show how metal oxides react with acids. Copy and complete the equations by replacing each fish or banana with the correct word(s).

(Look, I'm trying to make it interesting for you...)

a) tin oxide + hydrochloric acid ⟶ tin chloride +

b) zinc oxide + hydrochloric acid ⟶ + water

c) copper oxide + sulphuric acid ⟶ copper sulphate +

d) lead oxide + ⟶ lead sulphate +

e) + nitric acid ⟶ iron nitrate + water

f) + ⟶ magnesium nitrate +

Acids and Their Reactions

Q5   Copy the diagram below and then do these questions.

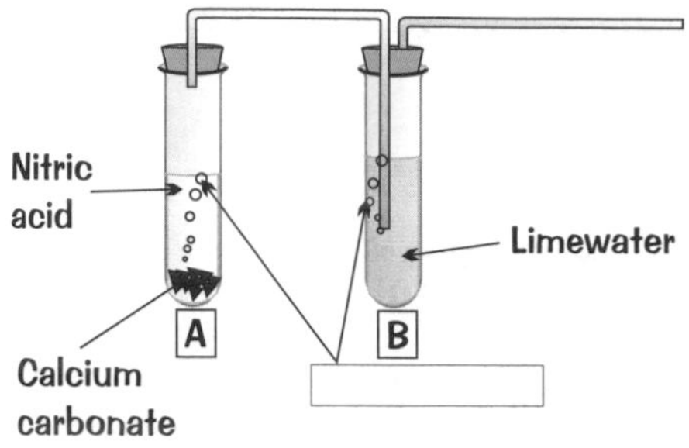

Nitric acid

Limewater

Calcium carbonate

A

B

a)   Complete the missing label on the diagram.

b)   What would you see happen to the limewater?

c)   What is the name of the new salt formed in tube A?

d)   What happens to this salt when it is formed?

e)   Use the words below to copy and complete the word equation for this reaction in tube A.

carbon dioxide, water, nitric acid, calcium nitrate, calcium carbonate

.... + ... $\longrightarrow$ .... + ... + ...

Q6   Zinc oxide and zinc carbonate are both white powders.

a)   Explain how you could use dilute sulphuric acid to tell them apart.
You can use any normal laboratory equipment.

b)   Write word equations for any reactions in part a).

c)   Write symbol equations for the word equations in b).

Q7   Copy and complete the equations below for the production of ammonium nitrate and ammonium chloride.

a) _____ + _____ $\rightarrow$ Ammonium Nitrate

b) _____ + _____ $\rightarrow$ Ammonium Chloride

Q8   Complete each of these general word equations about the reactions of dilute acids.

a)   ACID + METAL OXIDE $\longrightarrow$

b)   ACID + METAL CARBONATE $\longrightarrow$

c)   ACID + METAL HYDROGENCARBONATE $\longrightarrow$

d)   ACID + AMMONIA $\longrightarrow$

Top Tips

These reactions seem a bit complicated — but there's basically only <u>four types</u>. If you can write equations for acids with <u>metals</u>, <u>metal oxides</u>, <u>metal carbonates</u> and <u>metal hydrogencarbonates</u>, you'll sail through. Oh, and learn those ammonia ones too. Chemistry's all about learning — that's why everyone <u>loves it</u>.

Properties of Metals and Non-Metals

Q1   Look at the Periodic Table opposite.

Copy the table and shade in the area
that represents non-metals.

Q2   Iron is a metal and sulphur is a non-metal.

Copy and complete the table below for both, showing the differences
between metals and non-metals. Use the words in the box.

**You'll need to use
some more than once.**

> poor conductor   low   good conductor
> malleable   high   brittle

Element	Conducts heat	Conducts electricity	Melting Point	Boiling Point	Strength	Density
Iron						
Sulphur						

Q3   Melting and boiling points of metals are generally high.

a) How does this make them useful?

b) Which metal is the main exception to this? Give one use of it because of this property.

Q4   Match up each metal to its use:

| 1. Copper |
| 2. Lead |
| 3. Aluminium |
| 4. Gold |

| A. Used for jewellery |
| B. Used for aircraft |
| C. Used for wiring |
| D. Used to keep out radiation |

Q5   a) What is the name given to a mixture of metals?

b) Why do we mix metals together?

Q6   Use the table opposite to answer these questions:

a) Draw a bar chart showing the melting
points of the metals in the table.

b) Explain why tungsten is used in light bulbs.

Metal	Melting Point (°C)
Aluminium	659
Copper	1083
Gold	1064
Iron	1540
Lead	328
Tin	232
Tungsten	3410

Q7   Most non-metals do not conduct electricity.

a) What is the general name given to non-conducting materials?

H b) Explain why non-metals do not conduct electricity.

c) Name an exception to this rule.

The Reactivity Series of Metals

Q1   The reactivity series is a list of metals.

a) Put these metals in order of reactivity, starting with the most reactive first:

| potassium | gold | aluminium | silver | lead | sodium | iron | copper | zinc |

b) Match the following metals to the correct statement (use ewach statement only once).

1) Potassium	A) Will not react with water or dilute acid
2) Copper	B) Usually found alone (not combined with anything)
3) Iron	C) Very reactive metal
4) Gold	D) Corrodes in air fairly easily forming a substance called rust

Q2   Between which elements are **a)** carbon and **b)** hydrogen, in the above reactivity series?

Q3   Potassium has one electron in its outer shell, which is lost easily.

a) Roughly where in the reactivity series would you expect to find potassium?

b) Name two elements that could be above potassium in the reactivity series.

c) Using the information given below, place metals X and Y in the correct position in the reactivity series to the right.

Metal X —   Very reactive, burns in air readily to form a layer of oxide. Reacts violently in water but does not ignite the hydrogen produced.

Metal Y —   Corrodes very slowly, needs carbon for extraction from ore.

Potassium
Magnesium
Iron
Gold
Platinum

Q4   The table opposite contains information about metals.

Copy and complete the table, using your own words to explain what happens when each metal is heated in air.

Metal	Reaction when heated in air	Reaction with water
Calcium		
Zinc		
Iron		
Copper	slow reaction	
Silver		
Potassium		
Gold		
Magnesium		reacts with steam
Platinum	no reaction	
Lead		

Transition Metals

Q1 The transition metals have properties of typical metals.

   a) List the properties you would expect a typical metal to have.

   b) What other properties would you expect a transition element to have?

Q2 Name four transition metals you might come across everyday and where you would find them.

Q3 The transition metals form a block in the Periodic Table, rather than fall into groups like the other elements.

   Where are they found in the Periodic Table?

Q4 A metal "X" has a high melting point, can form 2^+ or 3^+ ions, and reacts slowly over a long time with water.

   Explain why you would put this in the transition element block rather than in Group II.

Q5 Match the correct colour to each of these compounds:

| 1) Chromium compounds |
| 2) Manganese compounds |
| 3) Copper compound |
| 4) Magnesium compounds |
| 5) Sodium compounds |

| A) White |
| B) Yellow / orange |
| C) Blue |
| D) Purple |
| E) White |

Q6 Human blood contains iron and is red.

   a) What colour would you expect Fe_2O_3 to be?

   b) Some species of spiders' blood contains copper. What **colour** might it be?

H Q7 The transition metal elements often have more than just one ion. For example, iron can be Iron(II) — Fe^{2+} or Iron(III) — Fe^{3+}. The number in brackets refers to the metal ion charge.

Copy and complete the table, giving the formula and charge on the transition element ion in each case. One has been done for you.

Compound	Formula	Charge on Ion
a) Iron(II) oxide		
b) Iron(III) chloride		
c) Iron(III) bromide	$FeBr_3$	Fe^{3+}
d) Copper(II) oxide		
e) Copper(I) chloride		
f) Copper(II) chloride		
g) Iron(III) iodide		

Top Tips

Don't be thrown by the name — transition metals have the same properties you would expect other metals to have. You need to be able to recognise which metal ion goes with which colour compound and be able to come up with some uses for common transition metals. Only then may you sleep easy.

Rates of Reaction

Q1   **Place** these chemical reactions **in order** of their speed, starting with the fastest reaction:

> Frying an egg   Striking a match   A car rusting   Concrete setting   Digesting food

Q2   When measuring the rate of a chemical reaction you can measure either the disappearance of reactant or the production of the product. Look at the apparatus below:

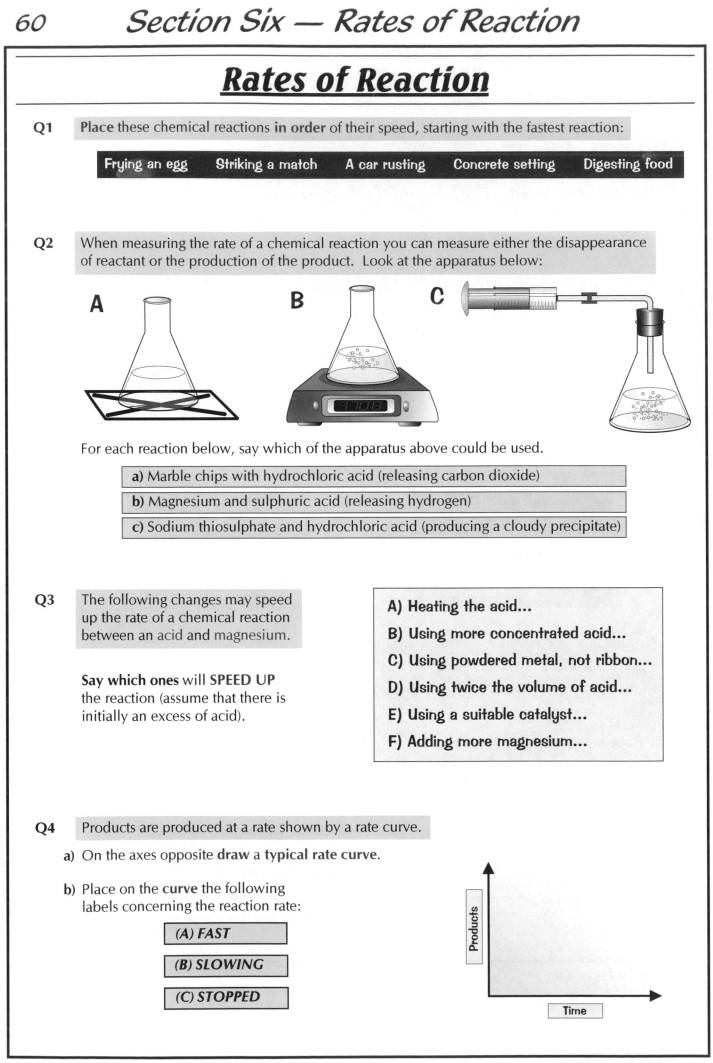

A   B   C

For each reaction below, say which of the apparatus above could be used.

> **a)** Marble chips with hydrochloric acid (releasing carbon dioxide)

> **b)** Magnesium and sulphuric acid (releasing hydrogen)

> **c)** Sodium thiosulphate and hydrochloric acid (producing a cloudy precipitate)

Q3   The following changes may speed up the rate of a chemical reaction between an acid and magnesium.

Say which ones will **SPEED UP** the reaction (assume that there is initially an excess of acid).

> A) Heating the acid...
>
> B) Using more concentrated acid...
>
> C) Using powdered metal, not ribbon...
>
> D) Using twice the volume of acid...
>
> E) Using a suitable catalyst...
>
> F) Adding more magnesium...

Q4   Products are produced at a rate shown by a rate curve.

a) On the axes opposite **draw** a **typical rate curve**.

b) Place on the **curve** the following labels concerning the reaction rate:

> (A) FAST

> (B) SLOWING

> (C) STOPPED

Products

Time

Collision Theory

Q1 Use your knowledge of reaction rates to **copy and complete** the text and diagrams below.

> **Fill the blank words (use more than once)**
> moderate   surface area   faster   collide
> particles   collision theory   concentration
> energy   catalyst   more often
> successful   collision

> **Diagram labels**
> FAST   SLOW   HIGH CONCENTRATION
> LOW CONCENTRATION   LARGE SURFACE AREA
> CATALYST PRESENT

a) Particles can only react if they _____ with enough _____ for the reaction to take place. This is called the _____ _____. There are four factors that can change the rate of a chemical reaction; temperature, _____, surface area and the use of a suitable _____.

b) ## Temperature

Increasing the temperature will cause the particles to move _____, with more energy. They will therefore collide _____ _____ and with greater _____. These two things mean there are more successful collisions per second and therefore a _____ rate of reaction.

Fast	Slow
Hot	Cold

c) ## Concentration

Increasing the concentration of a reactant simply means there are more _____ which may collide and so react. More collisions means a _____ reaction.

Fast	

d) ## Surface Area

Using a powder instead of a lump means the _____ _____ is greater, which means a greater area of reactant is exposed and so available for a collision. More collisions means a _____ reaction.

| | Small surface area |

e) ## Catalysts

Use of a suitable catalyst means that the particles may react even if they collide with only _____ energy. This means more _____ collisions are likely. Some catalysts work because one of the particles is fixed to a surface. This makes the chance of a _____ more likely. More collisions means a _____ reaction.

| | Slow |
| | No catalyst present |

Top Tips

This collision theory stuff is what I call <u>real</u> science — <u>and</u> it makes sense — things only <u>react</u> if they collide with enough speed — anything that increases their <u>speed</u> or <u>number of collisions</u> will increase the rate. Make sure you know how it applies to <u>temperature</u>, <u>concentration</u>, <u>surface area</u> and <u>catalysts</u>.

Four Experiments on Rates of Reaction

Q1   Marble chips react with acid to produce carbon dioxide gas. This loss of gas means that the reaction can be followed by recording the mass every 30 seconds on a balance.

The experiment was repeated using different sized pieces of marble:

Experiment 1 — large chips

Experiment 2 — small chips

Experiment 3 — powdered marble

a) In carrying out this experiment, **what factors** must be kept constant?

b) Use the results in the tables to **work out** the **total mass lost** after every 30 seconds.

Experiment 1

Time (s)	Mass (g)	Mass Lost (g)
0	100	0
30	99.8	
60	99.6	
90	99.4	
120	99.2	
150	99.0	
180	98.8	
210	98.6	
240	98.45	
270	98.30	
300	98.20	
330	98.15	
360	98.15	

Experiment 2

Time (s)	Mass (g)	Mass Lost (g)
0	100	0
30	99.7	
60	99.4	
90	99.1	
120	98.8	
150	98.6	
180	98.4	
210	98.3	
240	98.2	
270	98.15	
300	98.15	
330	98.15	
360	98.15	

Experiment 3

Time (s)	Mass (g)	Mass Lost (g)
0	100	0
30	99.0	
60	98.5	
90	98.3	
120	98.2	
150	98.15	
180	98.15	
210	98.15	
240	98.15	
270	98.15	
300	98.15	
330	98.15	
360	98.15	

c) **Plot** the **mass lost** against **time** for all three experiments on the same axes.

d) Which experiment was the **fastest**?

e) **Explain** your answer to part **d)** in terms of particles and collisions.

f) Why do all the graphs finish at the **same point**?

Q2   A similar experiment can be carried out to investigate the effect of changing the temperature on the rate of reaction. The graph below shows results from such an experiment. The acid is increasingly warmer in experiments 1, 2 and 3.

a) What **simple conclusion** can you draw from these graphs?

b) What do you notice about the **change in the rate** of the reaction for an increase of 10°C?

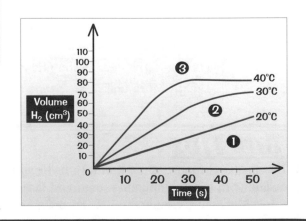

Four Experiments on Rates of Reaction

Q3 The reaction between sodium thiosulphate and hydrochloric acid produces a yellow precipitate of solid sulphur. This makes the solution cloudy and prevents us seeing clearly through it. The cross below the flask in the diagram will slowly disappear as the sulphur is produced.

In an experiment to investigate rates of reaction, the time taken for the cross to disappear was recorded.

50cm³ of sodium thiosulphate solution was used and 10cm³ of hydrochloric acid was added.

The experiment was repeated at different temperatures.

Temperature (°C)	20	30	40	50	60	70
Time taken (s)	163	87	43	23	11	5

a) **Plot a graph of these results**, with time taken on the vertical axis and temperature on the horizontal axis.

b) **Use the graph** to draw a simple conclusion about the effect of temperature on the time taken for the reaction to finish.

c) The rate of a reaction may be found by dividing 1 by the time taken (1/t). **Work out** the rate at each of the above temperatures.

d) **Plot a graph** of rate against temperature *(if the actual numbers for the rate value are too small to plot, use 'Rate × 1000' on the vertical axis)*.

e) **Use your graph** to draw a simple conclusion about the effect of temperature on the **RATE** of a chemical reaction.

f) Use your knowledge of the collision theory to **explain** your conclusion.

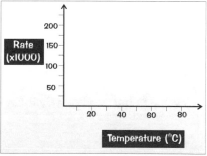

Q4 The breakdown of hydrogen peroxide may be catalysed by enzymes in living cells, particularly those in liver and potato. Study the graphs below, which show typical results from such an experiment.

a) Which of potato and liver is the more **effective** at breaking down hydrogen peroxide?

b) Which **two graphs** did you compare to answer **a)**?

c) What is the apparent effect of **boiling the living tissue**?

d) Why is minced liver **more effective** than the liver cube?

Legend:
① 1cm³ minced liver
② 1cm³ liver (cubed)
③ 1cm³ potato (cubed)
④ 1cm³ boiled potato
⑤ 1cm³ boiled liver

Top Tips

Well, there's **four** things that affect the <u>rates of reactions</u> — learning your <u>collision theory</u> should take care of that. Then it's just a case of learning the <u>three</u> ways of <u>monitoring</u> reaction rates. Just be sure you can <u>explain</u> them — and can draw a <u>graph</u> of the results against time for each of them.

Catalysts

Q1 The diagrams to the right show how 0.5g of zinc and 0.5g of copper react with dilute sulphuric acid.

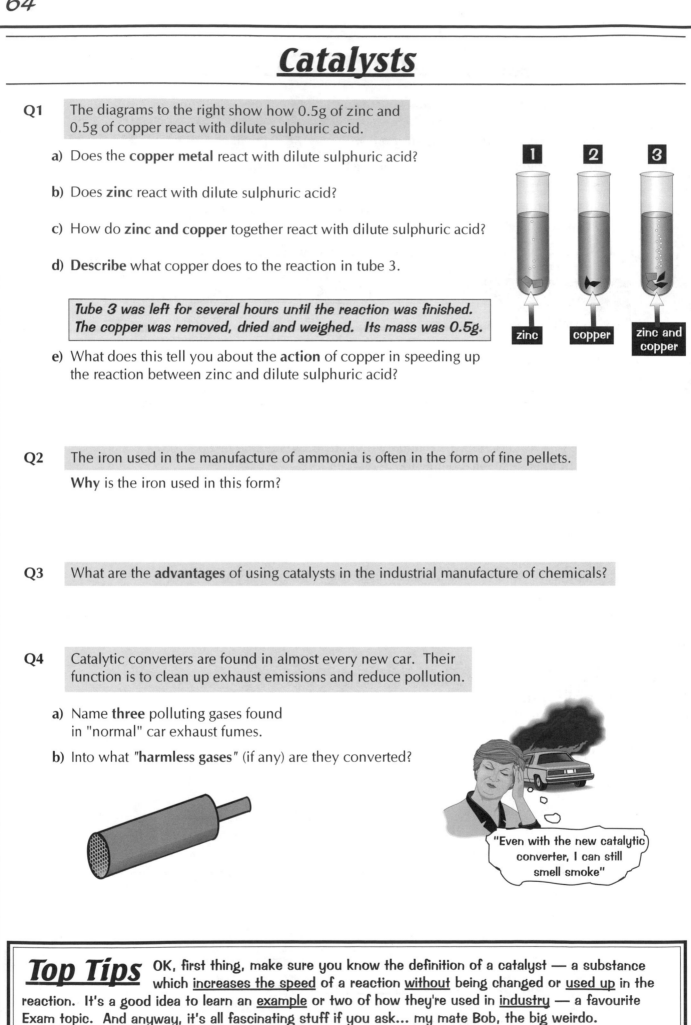

a) Does the **copper metal** react with dilute sulphuric acid?

b) Does **zinc** react with dilute sulphuric acid?

c) How do **zinc and copper** together react with dilute sulphuric acid?

d) Describe what copper does to the reaction in tube 3.

> *Tube 3 was left for several hours until the reaction was finished. The copper was removed, dried and weighed. Its mass was 0.5g.*

e) What does this tell you about the **action** of copper in speeding up the reaction between zinc and dilute sulphuric acid?

Q2 The iron used in the manufacture of ammonia is often in the form of fine pellets.

Why is the iron used in this form?

Q3 What are the **advantages** of using catalysts in the industrial manufacture of chemicals?

Q4 Catalytic converters are found in almost every new car. Their function is to clean up exhaust emissions and reduce pollution.

a) Name **three** polluting gases found in "normal" car exhaust fumes.

b) Into what *"harmless gases"* (if any) are they converted?

"Even with the new catalytic converter, I can still smell smoke"

Top Tips OK, first thing, make sure you know the definition of a catalyst — a substance which <u>increases the speed</u> of a reaction <u>without</u> being changed or <u>used up</u> in the reaction. It's a good idea to learn an <u>example</u> or two of how they're used in <u>industry</u> — a favourite Exam topic. And anyway, it's all fascinating stuff if you ask... my mate Bob, the big weirdo.

Enzymes

Q1 The experiment shown can be used to investigate enzyme activity.

Trypsin is an enzyme that catalyses the breakdown of protein. Photographic film has a protein layer that holds the silver compounds in place (these appear black). Different films use different proteins. If the protein is destroyed, this black layer falls off, leaving a clear plastic film.

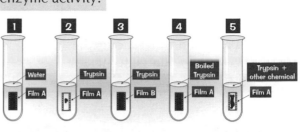

a) Copy the table opposite, then look at the tubes carefully. Compare the pairs suggested, writing your **conclusion** in your table.

b) Why was **Tube 1** included in the experiment?

Tubes	Possible conclusion
2 & 3	
2 & 4	
2 & 5	

Q2 The ability of trypsin to break down protein depends on the temperature. The experiment below investigates this. Strips of photographic film are each left for ten minutes in test tubes at the temperatures shown.

a) From these results, in what range is the **optimum temperature**?

b) Explain what happens to the enzyme at temperatures **above** the optimum temperature.

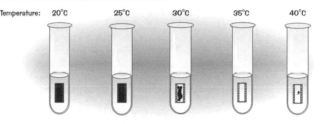

Q3 The browning of apples after being cut is an enzyme-catalysed reaction. An apple was cut into slices and left in different conditions.

a) What **conclusion** can be drawn by comparing results 1 and 2?

b) What **conclusion** can be drawn from results 1 and 3?

c) What does **Result 4** tell you about the nature of these catalysts?

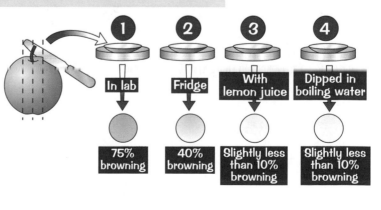

Uses of Enzymes

Q1 Starch is converted to sugar by several enzymes:

Which enzymes are the **best** at converting starch to sugar?

Enzyme	Percentage conversion after 30 minutes
Pepsin	0
Amylase	87
Trypsin	0
Maltase	67
Sucrase	42

Q2 Unfortunately the head teacher spilled custard down his clean white shirt. A group of Year 10 students offered to find the best way to get it clean. They cut up the shirt into squares and tested each with a different wash to find the best way to remove the stain.

Cut up!

0 Still dirty — 5 Spotless

Treatment	How clean?
A) Hand wash in cold water	0
B) Warm wash with ordinary powder	3
C) 70°C wash with "Ace bio powder"	3
D) 40°C wash with "Ace bio powder"	5
E) Cold wash with "Ace bio powder"	3

a) Which wash gave the **best result**?

b) What is the special ingredient in "*bio*" or "*biological*" powders?

c) Why did tests C and E not give a spotless result?

Q3 Bacteria are used in the food industry as well as yeast.

a) Milk is the starting material for which **two** major foods?

b) Why is **pasteurised milk** normally used instead of fresh milk?

c) For one of the foods in your answer to **a)**, **describe briefly** how it is made, and the importance of the fermentation process.

Q4 Loads of cream cakes were put in different places in the kitchen.

In which order should they be eaten if each is to be enjoyed as a **FRESH** cake?

Fridge

Freezer

Home Sweet Home

Current, Voltage and Resistance

These questions are about electric current — what it is, what makes it move and what tries to stop it.

Q1 Copy and complete the passage about electric current, choosing from the words below.

Words to use: electrons, charged, positive, metal, circuit

Current is a flow of _____ particles around a _____
Electric current can only flow if there are free _____ like in a _____,
where electrons flow throughout the structure of _____ ions.

Q2 Match the words with their correct description on the right:

a) current
b) resistance
c) voltage increase
d) amp (A)
e) ammeter
f) voltmeter
g) increase the resistance
h) volt (V)

Measures voltage

Unit of current

Flow of charged particles

Unit of voltage

Less current

Measures current

More current

Reduces current

Resistance is anything that reduces the current in a circuit. Electrical components and household electrical appliances all have some resistance.

Q3 A kettle is plugged into a 230V mains socket.
There is a current of 10A in its element.
Calculate the resistance of the element.

Q4 Find the current in a resistor of 18Ω
when it is connected to a 9V battery.

Q5 Copy and complete the table on the right:

Voltage(V)	Current(A)	Resistance(Ω)
	2.0	6.0
230		23.0
6	3.0	
1.5		15.0
12	4.0	
	1.5	5.0

The Standard Test Circuit

H **Q1** Copy and complete the sentences below by choosing the correct words and filling in the missing words:

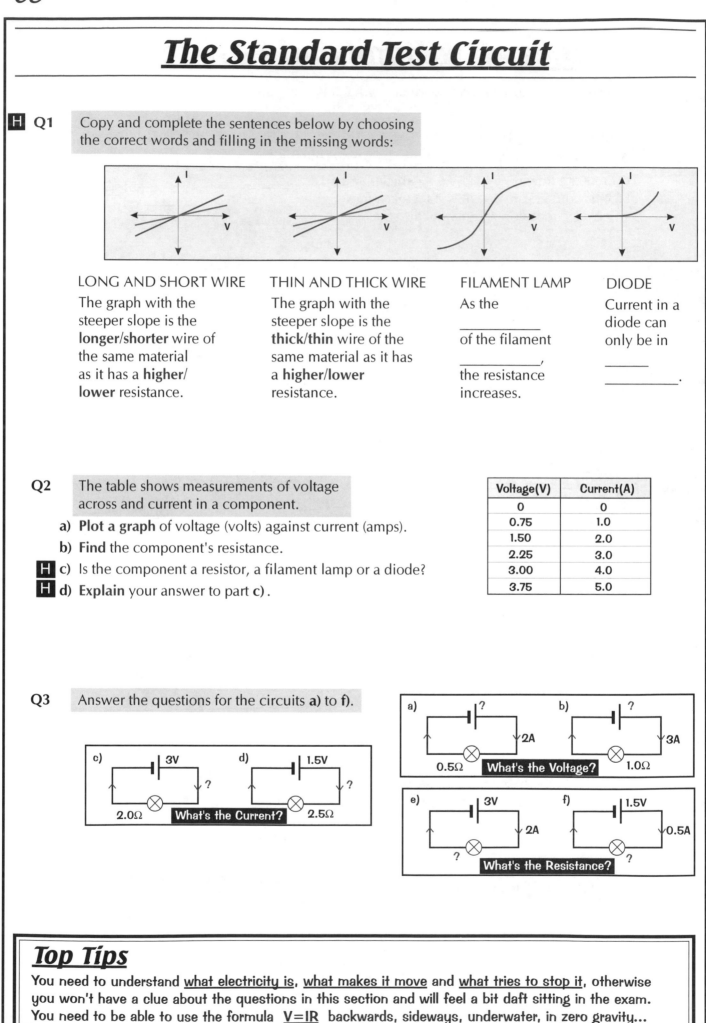

LONG AND SHORT WIRE
The graph with the steeper slope is the **longer/shorter** wire of the same material as it has a **higher/lower** resistance.

THIN AND THICK WIRE
The graph with the steeper slope is the **thick/thin** wire of the same material as it has a **higher/lower** resistance.

FILAMENT LAMP
As the _____ of the filament _____, the resistance increases.

DIODE
Current in a diode can only be in _____ _____.

Q2 The table shows measurements of voltage across and current in a component.

a) **Plot a graph** of voltage (volts) against current (amps).

b) **Find** the component's resistance.

H c) Is the component a resistor, a filament lamp or a diode?

H d) **Explain** your answer to part **c)**.

Voltage(V)	Current(A)
0	0
0.75	1.0
1.50	2.0
2.25	3.0
3.00	4.0
3.75	5.0

Q3 Answer the questions for the circuits **a)** to **f)**.

a) ? 2A 0.5Ω **What's the Voltage?**

b) ? 3A 1.0Ω

c) 3V ? 2.0Ω **What's the Current?**

d) 1.5V ? 2.5Ω

e) 3V 2A ? **What's the Resistance?**

f) 1.5V 0.5A ?

Top Tips

You need to understand <u>what electricity is</u>, <u>what makes it move</u> and <u>what tries to stop it</u>, otherwise you won't have a clue about the questions in this section and will feel a bit daft sitting in the exam. You need to be able to use the formula <u>**V=IR**</u> backwards, sideways, underwater, in zero gravity...

Circuit Symbols and Devices

Q1   Copy and complete the table for these electrical components.
You need to know these for your exam.

CIRCUIT SYMBOL	NAME FOR CIRCUIT SYMBOL	WHAT IT DOES
—┤├—		
H	LDR	
		Converts electrical energy into sound energy.
—Ⓥ—		
		Wire inside it breaks if the current is too high, protecting the appliance.
—▭—		
H	Thermistor	
	Open Switch	
H		Allows current in one direction only.
		Adjusted to alter the current in a circuit.
—Ⓜ—		
	Ammeter	

Q2 a) Design a circuit using all of these electrical components that would allow the speed
of the motor to be varied. The speed of the motor depends on the current through it.

Variable resistor   Motor   Ammeter   Battery

b)   *The variable resistor can be adjusted to slow the motor down.*
Explain this using the words resistance and current.

c)   When the motor is slowed down, what happens to the reading on the ammeter?

d)   Suggest how you could slow down the motor even more by changing one of the components.

Q3   Use the data in the table opposite to
plot a graph of resistance R, against
light intensity. Draw the best fit curve.

a) How does the resistance change as the light gets
brighter?

b) How does the resistance change as the light gets
dimmer?

H c) Looking at the slope of the graph,
comment on the rate of change of
resistance as the light intensity increases.

Resistance / Ω	Light Intensity / units
100,000	0.5
55,000	2.0
40,000	3.0
20,000	5.0
1000	7.5
100	10.0

H d) Give two uses for LDRs and explain how one of them works (drawing the circuit diagram may help).

Section Seven — Electricity

Series Circuits

Electrical devices can have dramatically different effects if they are arranged in <u>series</u> or <u>parallel</u>, as you know. The next two pages test if you <u>know the rules</u> for both types of circuit.

Use a pencil and ruler when drawing circuit diagrams so that they're clear, or else you'll only get half marks.

Q1   Draw a circuit diagram of a 6V battery, a switch and two lamps in series.

Q2   Draw a circuit diagram of a 12V power supply with a fuse and a heater in series.

Q3   The circuit below shows two lamps. Initially these lamps are of normal brightness.

Work out the brightness of the lamp(s) when the following modifications **a)** to **f)** are carried out.

a) One lamp is unscrewed.   Choose from: off, dimmer, normal or brighter.

b) One cell is turned around.

c) Another cell is added the same way around as the others.

d) Another cell is added the other way around to the others.

e) Another bulb is added.

f) Both cells are turned around.

Q4   Draw a circuit with a 2Ω and 4Ω resistor in series with a 6V battery.

a) What is the total resistance?

b) Calculate the current in the circuit.

Q5   The resistances of the resistors in this circuit are equal.
What are they if the ammeter reads 1A?

Q6   Christmas tree lights are a shining example of lamps in series.

a) What happens if one of the lamps is removed?

b) Find the total resistance of 10 lamps running off the mains (240V), if the current in each lamp is 0.5A. What is the resistance of each lamp?

Q7   Match each series combination **a) → d)** with the equivalent single resistor **1) → 4)**.

a) [1Ω]—[9Ω]   1) —[9Ω]—

b) [3Ω]—[4Ω]—[5Ω]   2) —[11Ω]—

c) [6Ω]—[3Ω]   3) —[12Ω]—

d) [5Ω]—[3Ω]—[3Ω]   4) —[10Ω]—

Q8 a) Find the total resistance in the circuit opposite.

b) What current will the ammeter show?

c) Calculate the voltmeter readings for Meter 1 and Meter 2.

Top Tips

<u>Series</u> circuits are really quite simple to understand. The components are connected <u>one after the other</u> between the +ve and −ve of the power supply (except the <u>voltmeters</u>, which are always connected in <u>parallel</u>). Also, <u>everything</u> in the circuit has the <u>same current</u> in it. Well, there you go — that's it in a nutshell.

Parallel Circuits

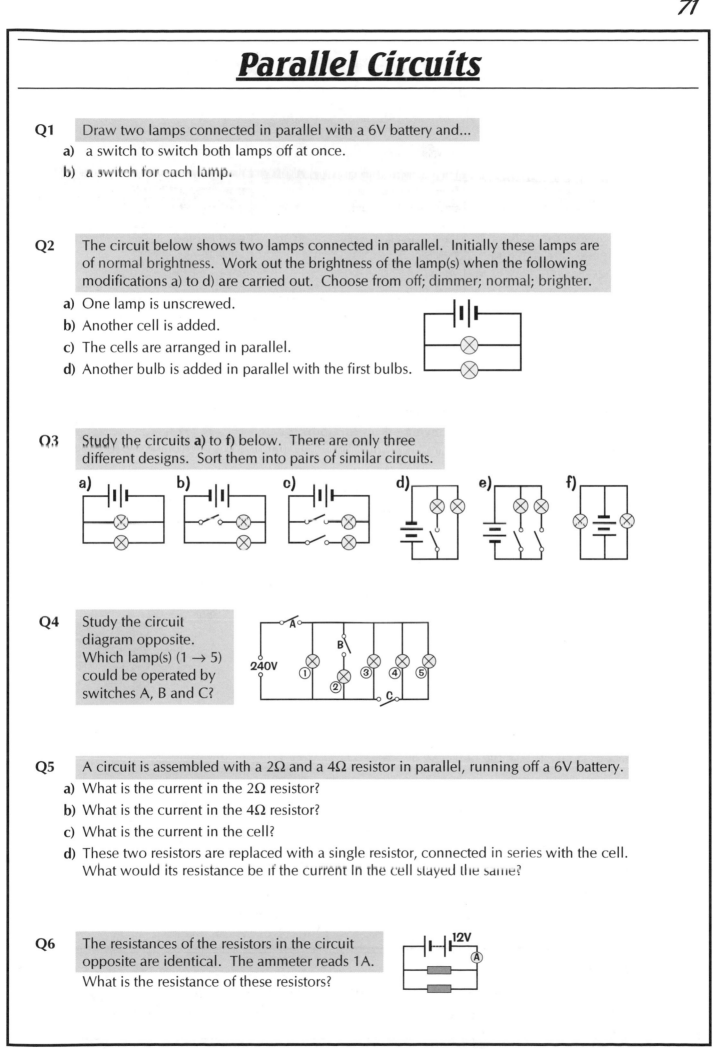

Q1   Draw two lamps connected in parallel with a 6V battery and...

    a) a switch to switch both lamps off at once.

    b) a switch for each lamp.

Q2   The circuit below shows two lamps connected in parallel. Initially these lamps are of normal brightness. Work out the brightness of the lamp(s) when the following modifications a) to d) are carried out. Choose from off; dimmer; normal; brighter.

    a) One lamp is unscrewed.

    b) Another cell is added.

    c) The cells are arranged in parallel.

    d) Another bulb is added in parallel with the first bulbs.

Q3   Study the circuits **a)** to **f)** below. There are only three different designs. Sort them into pairs of similar circuits.

Q4   Study the circuit diagram opposite. Which lamp(s) (1 → 5) could be operated by switches A, B and C?

Q5   A circuit is assembled with a 2Ω and a 4Ω resistor in parallel, running off a 6V battery.

    a) What is the current in the 2Ω resistor?

    b) What is the current in the 4Ω resistor?

    c) What is the current in the cell?

    d) These two resistors are replaced with a single resistor, connected in series with the cell. What would its resistance be if the current in the cell stayed the same?

Q6   The resistances of the resistors in the circuit opposite are identical. The ammeter reads 1A.

    What is the resistance of these resistors?

The Cost of Domestic Electricity

Q1 Look at these two electricity bills from Rippov Electricity:

a) Find the missing figures in these bills.

b) What is the scientific name for the term "units"?

c) If you were estimating the meter readings for a further quarter, what might they be?

Previous meter reading: **4 7 0 4 1**	Previous meter reading: **2 6 9 3 5**
Present meter reading: **4 7 5 2 5**	Present meter reading: **2 7 6 0 1**
Number of units used: ---------	Number of units used: ---------
Cost per unit (pence): 7.35	Cost per unit (pence): 7.35
Cost of electricity used: ---------	Cost of electricity used: ---------
Fixed quarterly charge: £9.49	Fixed quarterly charge: £9.49
Total bill: ---------	Total bill: ---------
VAT on Total bill at 8.0%: ---------	VAT on Total bill at 8.0%: ---------
Final total: £48.67	Final total: £63.12

d) If the bills were for the Summer quarter (May, June and July) what difference might you expect in a bill for the Winter quarter (November, December and January)? Explain your answer.

Q2 Copy and complete the table opposite to help you work out how many joules a hairdryer uses in one hour...

Power (kilowatts):	..........1 kW
Time switched on (in hours):	..........1 h
Power in watts:	....
Time switched on (seconds):	....
Energy used (in kilowatt hours):	....
Energy used (in joules):	....

Q3 Copy and complete this table. The first one is done for you.

Appliance	Rating(kW)	Time(h)	Energy (kWh)	Cost at 10p per unit
Storage Heaters	2	4	2 × 4 = 8	8 × 10 = 80p
Cooker	7	2		
1-bar Electric Fire	1	1.5		
Kettle	2	0.1		
Iron	1	1.2		
Refrigerator	0.12	24.0		
Lamp	0.06	6.0		
Cassette Player	0.012	2.0		

[Cost of electricity = power (kW) x time (h) x cost of 1kWh]

Q4 Find the cost (at 10p/unit) of using:

a) An electric drill, power 300W, for 2 hours.

b) A 20W hairstyling brush for 1/2 hour.

c) Two 100W electric lights on for 9 hours a day for a week.

d) A 900W toaster for 15 minutes every day for a month (30 days — it's September!).

e) Four 60W electric lights on 12 hours a day for an old-fashioned working week (5 days).

Top Tips

The <u>units</u> that electricity meters measure are <u>kilowatt-hours (kWh)</u>, and that means the <u>amount</u> of <u>electrical energy</u> used by a <u>1kW appliance</u> left on for <u>1 hour</u>. Don't be confused by the name, it isn't a measurement of power.

Mains Electricity — Plugs and Fuses

Q1 State the electrical hazards in each diagram below, and say what you would do to make each one safe:

a)   b)   c)

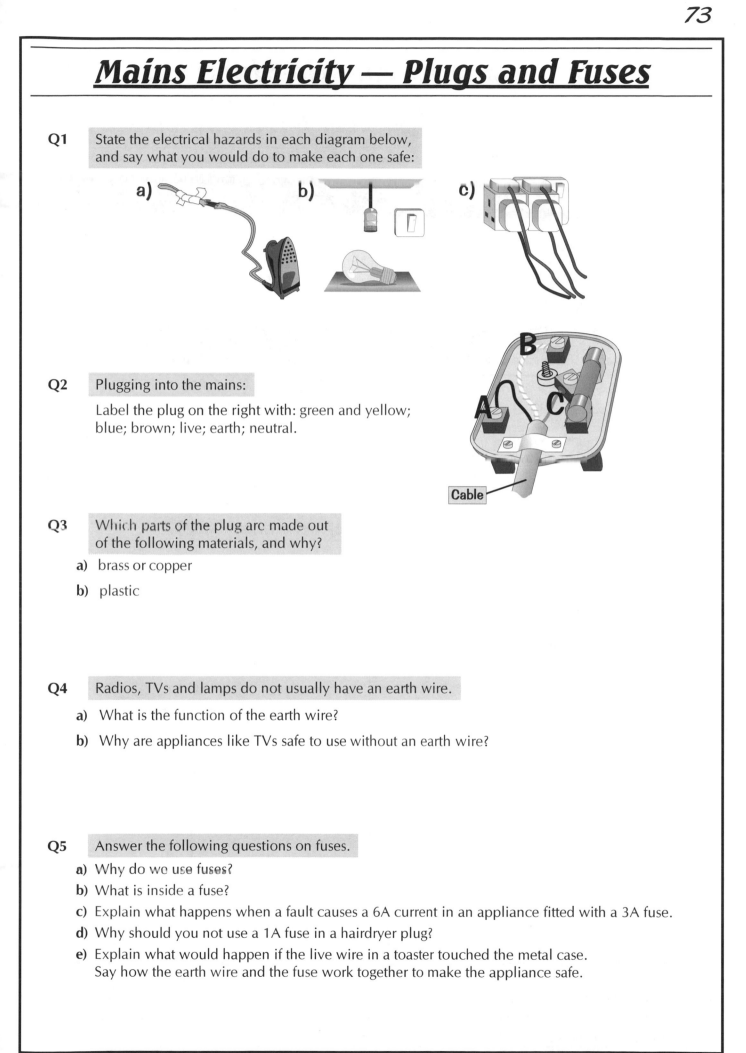

Q2 Plugging into the mains:

Label the plug on the right with: green and yellow; blue; brown; live; earth; neutral.

Cable

Q3 Which parts of the plug are made out of the following materials, and why?

a) brass or copper

b) plastic

Q4 Radios, TVs and lamps do not usually have an earth wire.

a) What is the function of the earth wire?

b) Why are appliances like TVs safe to use without an earth wire?

Q5 Answer the following questions on fuses.

a) Why do we use fuses?

b) What is inside a fuse?

c) Explain what happens when a fault causes a 6A current in an appliance fitted with a 3A fuse.

d) Why should you not use a 1A fuse in a hairdryer plug?

e) Explain what would happen if the live wire in a toaster touched the metal case. Say how the earth wire and the fuse work together to make the appliance safe.

The National Grid

Q1   *The diagram below shows how electricity is made in power stations, and sent to homes and industry.*

a) Complete the labels on the diagram.

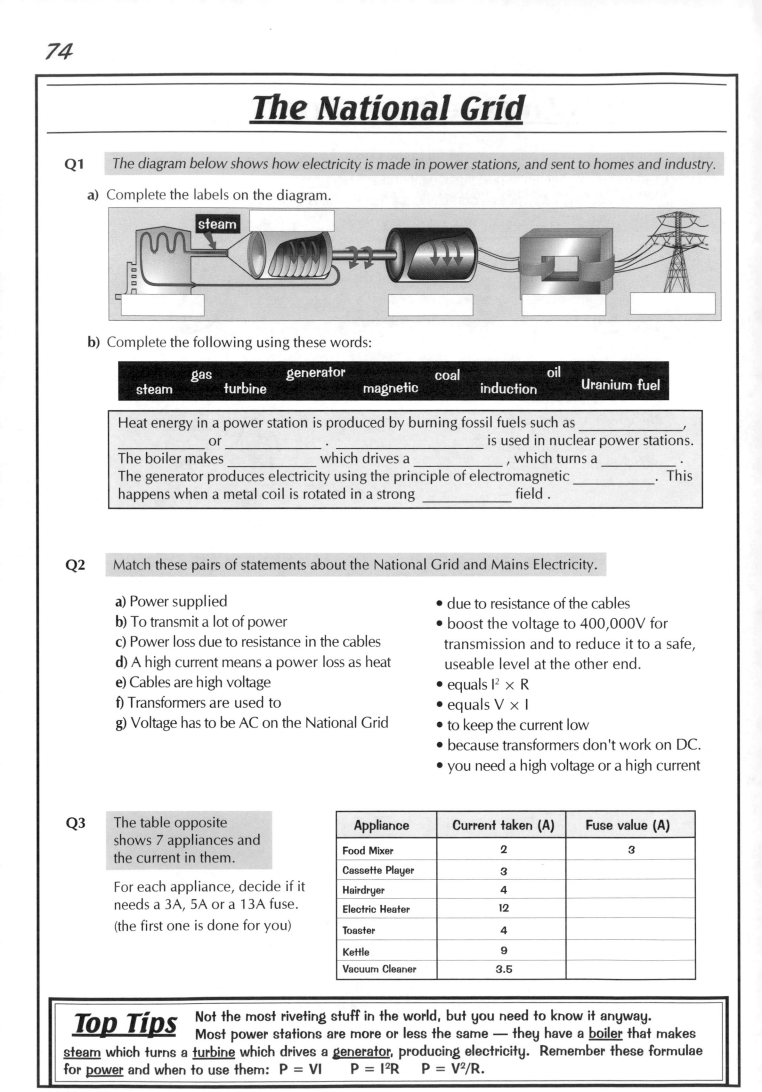

b) Complete the following using these words:

	gas	generator		coal		oil	
steam	turbine		magnetic		induction		Uranium fuel

> Heat energy in a power station is produced by burning fossil fuels such as _____,
> _____ or _____ . _____ is used in nuclear power stations.
> The boiler makes _____ which drives a _____ , which turns a _____ .
> The generator produces electricity using the principle of electromagnetic _____ . This
> happens when a metal coil is rotated in a strong _____ field .

Q2   Match these pairs of statements about the National Grid and Mains Electricity.

a) Power supplied
b) To transmit a lot of power
c) Power loss due to resistance in the cables
d) A high current means a power loss as heat
e) Cables are high voltage
f) Transformers are used to
g) Voltage has to be AC on the National Grid

- due to resistance of the cables
- boost the voltage to 400,000V for transmission and to reduce it to a safe, useable level at the other end.
- equals $I^2 \times R$
- equals $V \times I$
- to keep the current low
- because transformers don't work on DC.
- you need a high voltage or a high current

Q3   The table opposite shows 7 appliances and the current in them.

For each appliance, decide if it needs a 3A, 5A or a 13A fuse.

(the first one is done for you)

Appliance	Current taken (A)	Fuse value (A)
Food Mixer	2	3
Cassette Player	3	
Hairdryer	4	
Electric Heater	12	
Toaster	4	
Kettle	9	
Vacuum Cleaner	3.5	

Top Tips   Not the most riveting stuff in the world, but you need to know it anyway.
Most power stations are more or less the same — they have a <u>boiler</u> that makes
<u>steam</u> which turns a <u>turbine</u> which drives a <u>generator</u>, producing electricity. Remember these formulae
for <u>power</u> and when to use them: $P = VI$ $P = I^2R$ $P = V^2/R$.

Section Seven — Electricity

Waves — Basic Principles

Q1   Copy the following sentences and **fill in the gaps**.

H a)   There are two different types of wave motion: _____ and _____ .

b)   The number of waves per second passing a fixed point is called the _____ and is measured in _____ .

c)   The time taken for two adjacent crests to pass a fixed point is called the _____ and is measured in _____ .

d)   The maximum distance of particles from their resting position is called the _____ .

H e)   The highest point of a transverse wave is called a _____ .

H f)   The lowest point of a transverse wave is called a _____ .

H Q2   Describe the motion of the particles in an ocean wave.

H Q3   Describe the motion of the particles in a sound wave moving through air.

Q4   *You can send a wave along a piece of string by shaking one end up and down (see diagram).*

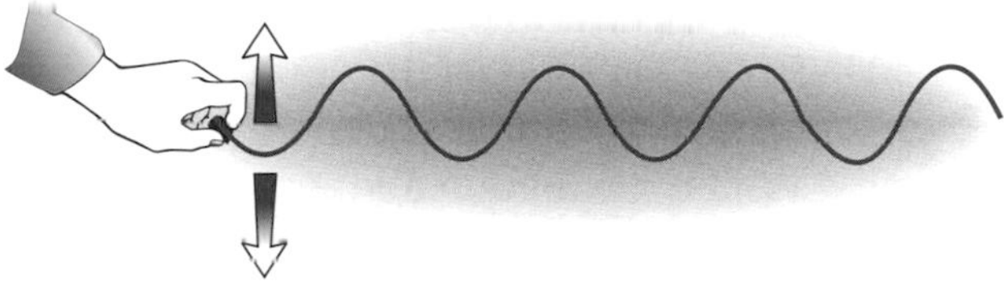

a)   What do we call the up and down movement of any point on the string?

b)   How would you increase the frequency of this wave?

c)   How would you increase its amplitude?

H d)   This wave is a transverse wave. Explain why a longitudinal wave of a similar frequency cannot be made to travel along the string.

Q5   The diagram below shows a piece of string with a wave travelling along it, as illustrated in **Q4**. There are beads attached to the string in positions A, B, C, D, E, F, G, H and I.

a)   Where on the diagram will the stationary string lie after the wave has died away?

H b)   Which bead(s) are:

   i)   at the crests?

   ii)   at troughs?

   iii)   moving up?

   iv)   moving down?

   v)   changing direction?

   vi)   stationary?

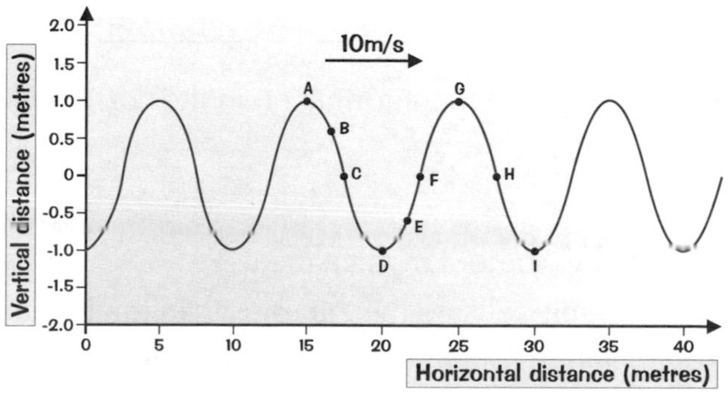

Top Tips

Don't forget the difference between <u>transverse</u> and <u>longitudinal</u> waves — you'll need to be able to give three examples of each type of wave. It's all good fun, this stuff — you know that deep down.

Sound and Ultrasound

Q1   What has to happen for a sound wave to be created?

Q2   What **vibrates** in the objects below to start a sound?

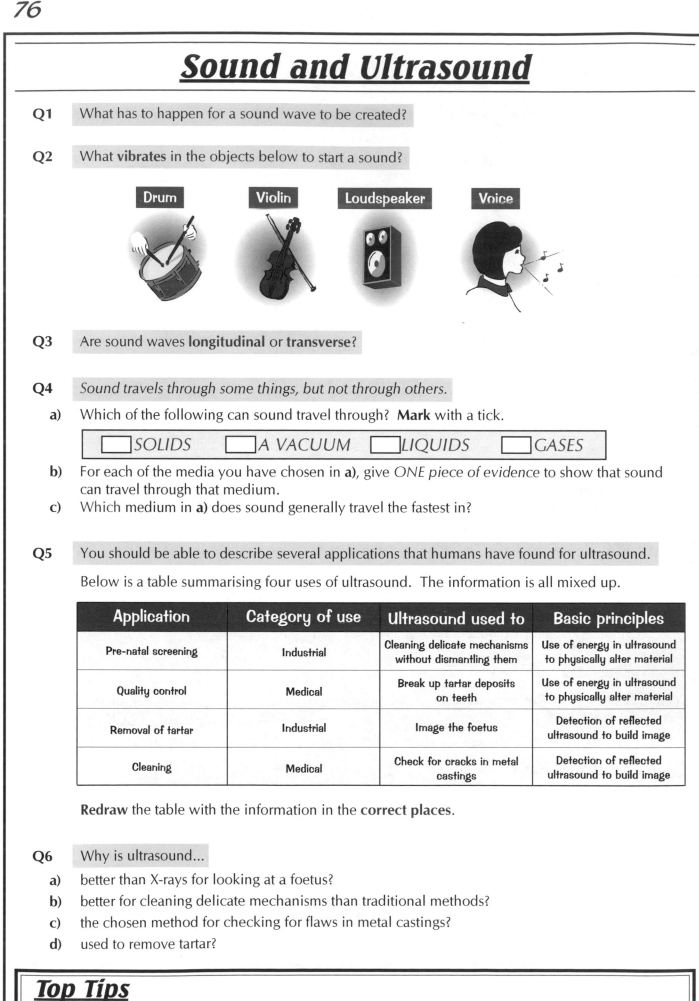

Drum   Violin   Loudspeaker   Voice

Q3   Are sound waves **longitudinal** or **transverse**?

Q4   *Sound travels through some things, but not through others.*

a)   Which of the following can sound travel through? **Mark** with a tick.

☐ SOLIDS   ☐ A VACUUM   ☐ LIQUIDS   ☐ GASES

b)   For each of the media you have chosen in **a)**, give *ONE piece of evidence* to show that sound can travel through that medium.

c)   Which medium in **a)** does sound generally travel the fastest in?

Q5   You should be able to describe several applications that humans have found for ultrasound.

Below is a table summarising four uses of ultrasound. The information is all mixed up.

Application	Category of use	Ultrasound used to	Basic principles
Pre-natal screening	Industrial	Cleaning delicate mechanisms without dismantling them	Use of energy in ultrasound to physically alter material
Quality control	Medical	Break up tartar deposits on teeth	Use of energy in ultrasound to physically alter material
Removal of tartar	Industrial	Image the foetus	Detection of reflected ultrasound to build image
Cleaning	Medical	Check for cracks in metal castings	Detection of reflected ultrasound to build image

Redraw the table with the information in the **correct places**.

Q6   Why is ultrasound...

a)   better than X-rays for looking at a foetus?

b)   better for cleaning delicate mechanisms than traditional methods?

c)   the chosen method for checking for flaws in metal castings?

d)   used to remove tartar?

Top Tips
You have to know what makes sound waves and how they travel — remember that sound won't travel in a vacuum. And be sure you can say what the <u>benefits</u> are of using ultrasound.

Reflection: a Property of all Waves

Q1 *Like sound, light can be reflected off surfaces. Copy and complete the sentences below.*

a) Some objects give out their own light. All other objects we see because they
_____ light.

b) Some objects reflect light without sending it off in many different directions. This is
called a _____ reflection and objects which do this look _____.

c) Most objects send the reflected light in many different directions, giving a
_____ reflection. These objects look _____.

d) The law of reflection states that "the angle of _____ is _____ to
the angle of _____."

Q2 What is the name for the line drawn at right angles to a mirror surface?

Q3 The diagrams 1, 2 and 3 shows rays arriving at a surface.

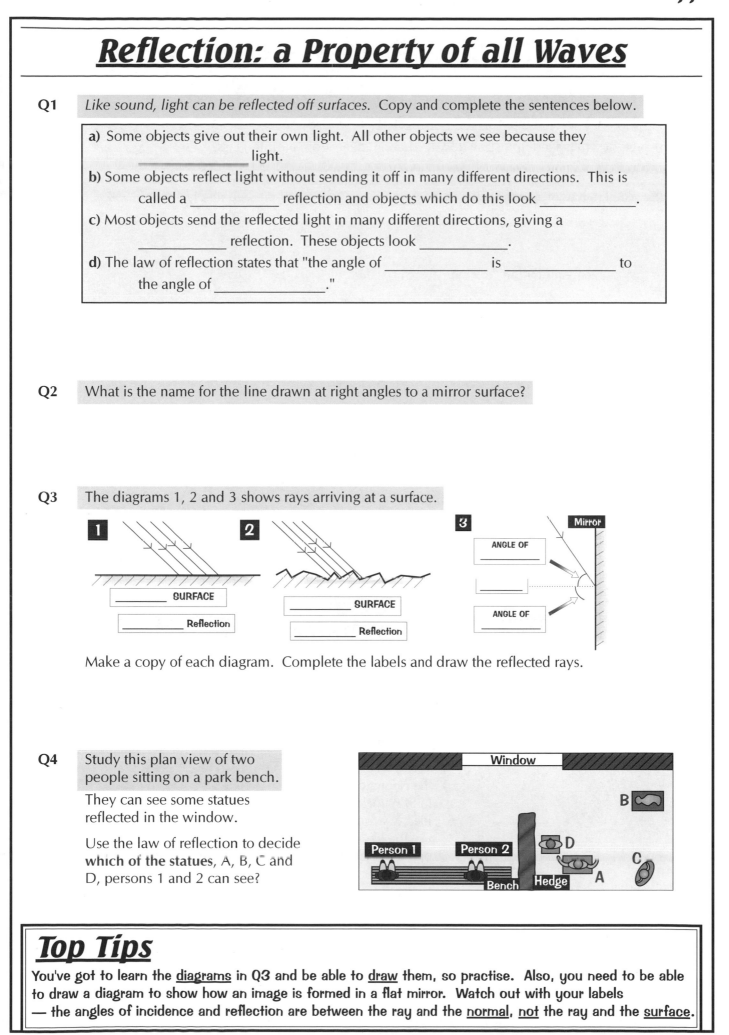

Make a copy of each diagram. Complete the labels and draw the reflected rays.

Q4 Study this plan view of two
people sitting on a park bench.

They can see some statues
reflected in the window.

Use the law of reflection to decide
which of the statues, A, B, C and
D, persons 1 and 2 can see?

Top Tips

You've got to learn the <u>diagrams</u> in Q3 and be able to <u>draw</u> them, so practise. Also, you need to be able
to draw a diagram to show how an image is formed in a flat mirror. Watch out with your labels
— the angles of incidence and reflection are between the ray and the <u>normal</u>, <u>not</u> the ray and the <u>surface</u>.

Refraction: A Property of all Waves

Q1 **Copy the following sentences and fill in the gaps _or_ choose the correct words.**

a) Light travels at different _____ in different media.

b) Light will [speed up / slow down] when it travels from air into glass.

c) When the light goes back into air it will [speed up / slow down].

d) The change of speed occurs at the _____ of the two media.

Q2 What is meant by the **"normal"** to a surface?

Q3 Does the **frequency** of light change as it enters a different medium?

Q4 Study the rays in the two diagrams on the right.

a) In Diagram 1, a ray **enters** a glass block. Which ray, X, Y or Z, shows how it would continue?

b) In Diagram 2, a ray **leaves** the block. Which ray, A, B or C, shows its path correctly?

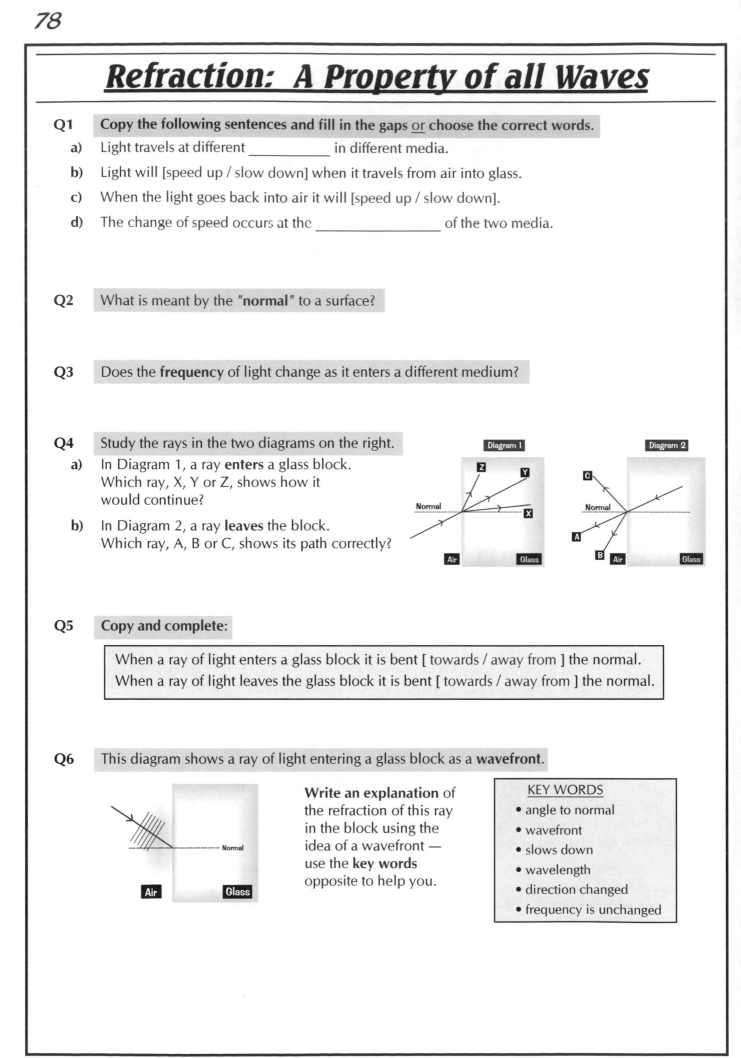

Q5 **Copy and complete:**

> When a ray of light enters a glass block it is bent [towards / away from] the normal.
> When a ray of light leaves the glass block it is bent [towards / away from] the normal.

Q6 This diagram shows a ray of light entering a glass block as a **wavefront.**

Write an explanation of the refraction of this ray in the block using the idea of a wavefront — use the **key words** opposite to help you.

KEY WORDS
• angle to normal
• wavefront
• slows down
• wavelength
• direction changed
• frequency is unchanged

Total Internal Reflection

Q1 **Copy and complete** this paragraph about total internal reflection.

> "Total internal reflection happens when light is travelling in a material like [glass / air]
> and comes to the [edge / middle] of the block. If the light meets the boundary at a large
> angle to the [edge / normal], the ray is [refracted / diffracted / reflected], not
> [refracted / reflected]. The angle at which total internal reflection begins is called the
> [critical / incident / normal] angle and is about [22 / 42 / 90] degrees in glass."

Q2 The diagram shows two identical glass blocks with a ray entering at two different angles.

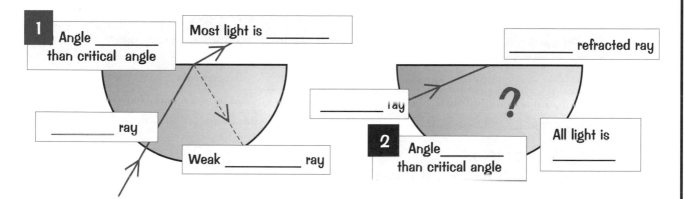

a) **Copy** Diagram 1 and **complete** the labelling.

b) **Copy** Diagram 2. **Draw** the reflected ray and normal inside the block and **complete** the labelling.

Q3 a) Draw a diagram of an optical fibre, showing:

> • the layers of the fibre
> • the light ray travelling along it (show 3 or 4 reflections)

Mark with arrows where total internal reflection occurs.

b) State the **advantages** of optical fibres over wires for carrying information.

Q4 **Describe** what an endoscope is, and give a use of an endoscope in a hospital.
Can you think of one other use of total internal reflection?

Top Tips

Prisms and lenses use refraction. You need to know <u>which way</u> the colours go in the rainbow from a
prism — think about which colour is refracted <u>most</u> and which is refracted <u>least</u>. Remember that
Total Internal Reflection happens when the light is in something <u>dense</u> like glass or water.

Digital and Analogue Signals

Q1   Information such as speech or music can be converted into electrical signals.

    a)   What are the **two** ways of transmitting this information?

    b)   Write down the ways in which they are **different**.

    c)   **List three** examples of devices which use each type of signal.

Q2   Decide whether the following statements are **true or false**. If false, write out the correct version.

    a)   The **amplitude** and **frequency** of **digital** signals vary continuously.

    b)   **Digital** pulses can take one of only **two** values.

    c)   Clocks and dimmer switches can **both** be **analogue** devices.

    d)   Clocks and on/off switches can **both** be **digital** devices.

    e)   The problem with **digital** signals is that they lose quality relatively quickly.

    f)   **Digital** signals are capable of transmitting more information than analogue ones (within a given time).

Q3   Signals often need to be **amplified** along their route or at their destination.

    a)   Why is this necessary?

    b)   What else usually happens to a signal between its source and its destination? (**Hint:** it picks up something unwanted).

Q4   Rearrange these pictures into **two sets** (including arrows) to show:

    a)   Analogue signals picking up noise and then being amplified.

    b)   Digital signals picking up noise and then being amplified.

H Q5   It is possible to change a digital signal to an analogue one and vice versa.

    a)   What are the names of the two devices used to do this?

    b)   Give an example of something that contains both of them.

Top Tips

This is all very practical, so you can bet you'll get a question on it.
Make sure you know the __differences__ between analogue and digital signals, and __why__ digital signals are usually better. And "because we can watch the footy and loads of cool movies" is not an Exam answer.

Diffraction: A Property of all Waves

Q1   **Copy and complete** the following sentences.

a) Waves will _____ when they go through a _____ or past an _____.

b) This effect is called _____

c) The _____ the gap the more diffraction there is.

d) If the gap is about the same size as the _____ of the wave, a _____ shaped wave will be produced.

Q2   The following diagrams show plane waves approaching an obstacle.

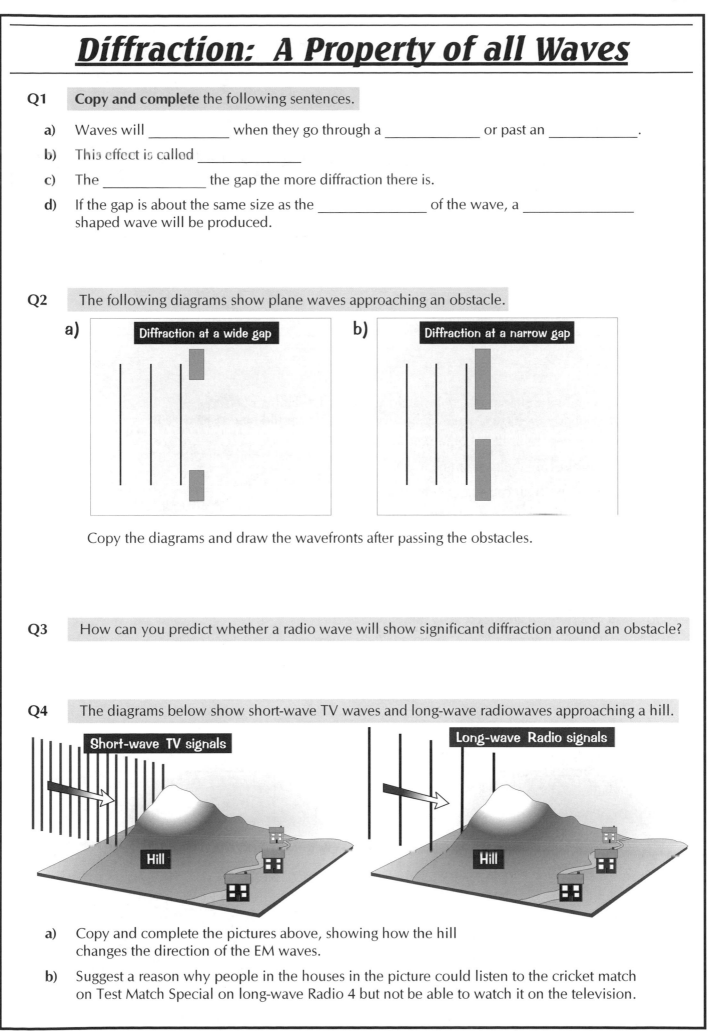

a) **Diffraction at a wide gap**

b) **Diffraction at a narrow gap**

Copy the diagrams and draw the wavefronts after passing the obstacles.

Q3   How can you predict whether a radio wave will show significant diffraction around an obstacle?

Q4   The diagrams below show short-wave TV waves and long-wave radiowaves approaching a hill.

Short-wave TV signals

Long-wave Radio signals

Hill

Hill

a) Copy and complete the pictures above, showing how the hill changes the direction of the EM waves.

b) Suggest a reason why people in the houses in the picture could listen to the cricket match on Test Match Special on long-wave Radio 4 but not be able to watch it on the television.

The Electromagnetic Spectrum

Q1   Copy and complete the following paragraphs about electromagnetic waves.

a) Electromagnetic (EM) waves form a continuous_____. For a given _____ all EM waves travel with roughly the same _____. There are _____ main types of EM wave. The correct order for these types of EM wave is (beginning with longest wavelength): _____, _____, _____, _____, _____, _____ and _____.

b) _____ waves have the lowest frequency and the _____ wavelength, and _____ have the highest frequency and the _____ wavelength. Our eyes are sensitive to EM waves from the _____ spectrum only.

Q2   For each of the statements a) to j) below, state whether it is true or false. If it is false, write down what the highlighted words should be replaced with.

a)   **Microwaves** are used to communicate with satellites.

b)   **Microwaves** are the same thing as heat radiation.

c)   **Gamma rays** both cause and cure cancer.

d)   **Only visible light** will show diffraction.

e)   **Radio waves** can have wavelengths of many metres.

f)   **X-rays** are used to take pictures of bones because they are relatively safe.

g)   **Infrared** radiation causes skin cancer.

h)   **Microwaves** are absorbed by water.

i)   **Long wave radiowaves** are able to diffract long distances round the Earth.

j)   **Visible light** has a wavelength of about a ten thousandth of a millimetre.

Q3   The diagram shows parts of the electromagnetic spectrum and wavelengths for the different radiations. However, they are all mixed up.

a)   **Draw** your own diagram of a spectrum, but with the types of radiation and wavelengths in the correct order, from the shortest to the longest wavelength.

b)   How many times longer is a typical visible light wave compared with an X-ray wave?

c)   How many times longer is a microwave compared with a typical visible light wave?

10^{-5} m (0.01 mm)

10^{-7} m

INFRA-RED

10^{-2} m (1 cm)

MICRO-WAVES

GAMMA RAYS

ULTRA-VIOLET

10^{-10} m

X-RAYS

RADIO WAVES

10^{-8} m

10^{-12} m

VISIBLE LIGHT

10^{0} m (1 m)

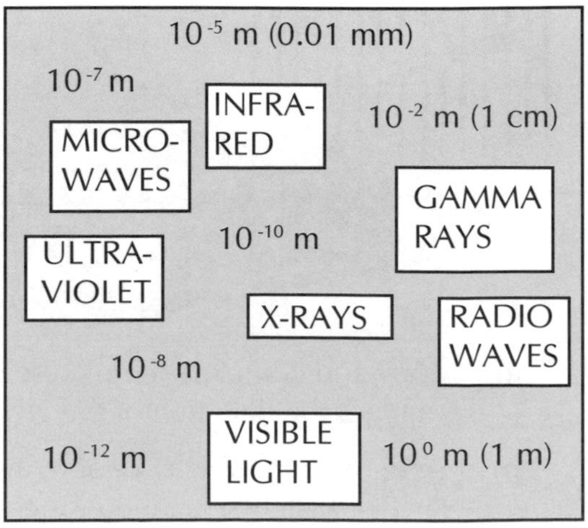

Uses of EM Radiation

Q1 An electromagnetic wave is drawn on an A4 piece of paper so that one wavelength fills the page. You are told it is drawn actual size.

What type of EM wave could the drawing represent?

Q2 This table is all mixed up. **Redraw** the table with the information in the **correct** places:

Type of Radiation	Effects on Living Tissue	Uses
Gamma	• probably none	• communication • broadcasting • radar
X-Ray	• heating of water in tissues can cause "burning"	• imaging internal structures in the body
UV	• kills living cells in high doses • lower doses can cause cells to beoome cancerous • causes tanning	• fluorescent tubes • tanning • security marking
Visible	• kills living cells in high doses • lower doses can cause cells to become cancerous • kills cancerous cells	• kill bacteria in food • sterilise medical equipment • treat tumours
IR	• kills living cells in high doses • lower doses can cause cells to become cancerous	• radiant heaters • grills • remote controls • thermal imaging
Microwave	• causes burning of tissues	• satellite communication • cooking
Radio	• activates sensitive cells in the retina	• seeing • optical fibre communication

Top Tips

Lots of juicy facts. It's all important, so don't skip bits. To help you learn the order of the EM spectrum you could use this phrase — or perhaps invent a better one. Rabid Monkeys In Violet Underpants eXterminate Gibbons. Remember that the speed of all **EM** waves in a vacuum is the same.

The Planets

Q1   This question consists of a number of statements about the Solar System.

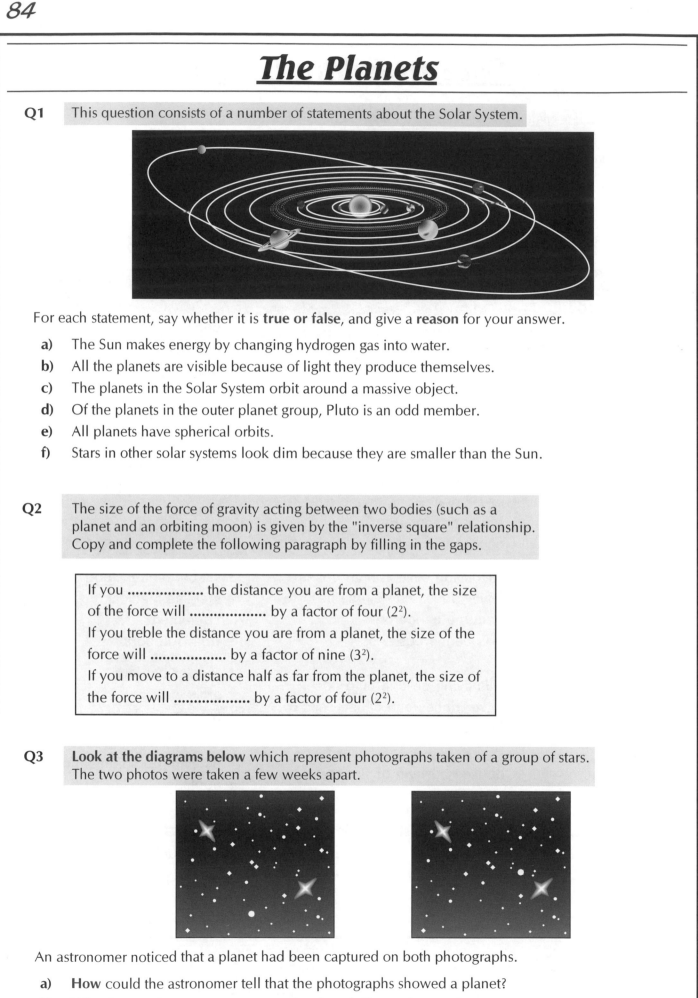

For each statement, say whether it is **true or false**, and give a **reason** for your answer.

a)   The Sun makes energy by changing hydrogen gas into water.

b)   All the planets are visible because of light they produce themselves.

c)   The planets in the Solar System orbit around a massive object.

d)   Of the planets in the outer planet group, Pluto is an odd member.

e)   All planets have spherical orbits.

f)   Stars in other solar systems look dim because they are smaller than the Sun.

Q2   The size of the force of gravity acting between two bodies (such as a planet and an orbiting moon) is given by the "inverse square" relationship. Copy and complete the following paragraph by filling in the gaps.

> If you .... the distance you are from a planet, the size of the force will .... by a factor of four (2^2).
>
> If you treble the distance you are from a planet, the size of the force will .... by a factor of nine (3^2).
>
> If you move to a distance half as far from the planet, the size of the force will .... by a factor of four (2^2).

Q3   **Look at the diagrams below** which represent photographs taken of a group of stars. The two photos were taken a few weeks apart.

An astronomer noticed that a planet had been captured on both photographs.

a)   **How** could the astronomer tell that the photographs showed a planet?

b)   Why does a planet appear to cross the sky **relative** to the stars?

c)   What is the **name** given to the fixed pattern of stars recognised by astronomers?

Satellites and Comets

Q1 Artificial ssatellites have been used for different purposes since the first successful launch in the 1950s. Today, satellites play an important role in our lives. The following statements can describe the motion of satellites.

> A. a high orbit
> B. a low orbit
> C. geosynchronous
> D. move across the sky
> E. above the atmosphere
> F. in a polar orbit
> G. in an equatorial orbit
> H. orbits in a few hours
> I. orbits in 24 hours

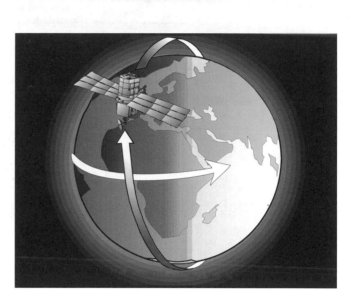

Which of the statements above will apply to:

a) communications satellites?

b) most weather satellites?

c) spy satellites?

d) satellites broadcasting TV pictures?

Q2 If the space shuttle is in orbit, more than one Earth-based station is needed to communicate with it. Why would **one station** be no good?

Like all members of the Solar System, comets follow tracks around the Sun.

Q3 What name is given to the **path** followed by a comet?

Q4 Draw a diagram showing the **shape of the path** followed by a comet around the Sun.

Comet

Q5 Give the **name of the shape** formed by the path of a comet.

Q6 **Explain how** this shape differs from the paths followed by the planets.

Top Tips

First of all, you need to know <u>why</u> people put satellites up there in the first place. Make sure you learn the difference between <u>geostationary</u> and <u>polar orbit</u> satellites — it's important, because you have to be able to say which <u>orbits</u> are used for which <u>purposes</u>. It's all there in Question 1.

Section Eight — Waves and Outer Space

Searching for Life on Other Planets

We may not be alone in the Universe — there may well be life elsewhere.
Scientists are using a variety of methods to try and find evidence of extraterrestrial life.

Q1   There are certain **conditions** that are necessary for **life** to exist on other planets.
Copy the diagram below, **filling in** the blank spaces on the diagram below, using these words:

| temperature | hot | water | cold | liquid |

It's likely that _____ is needed in _____ form.

The _____ must be just right — not too ____ and not too ____.

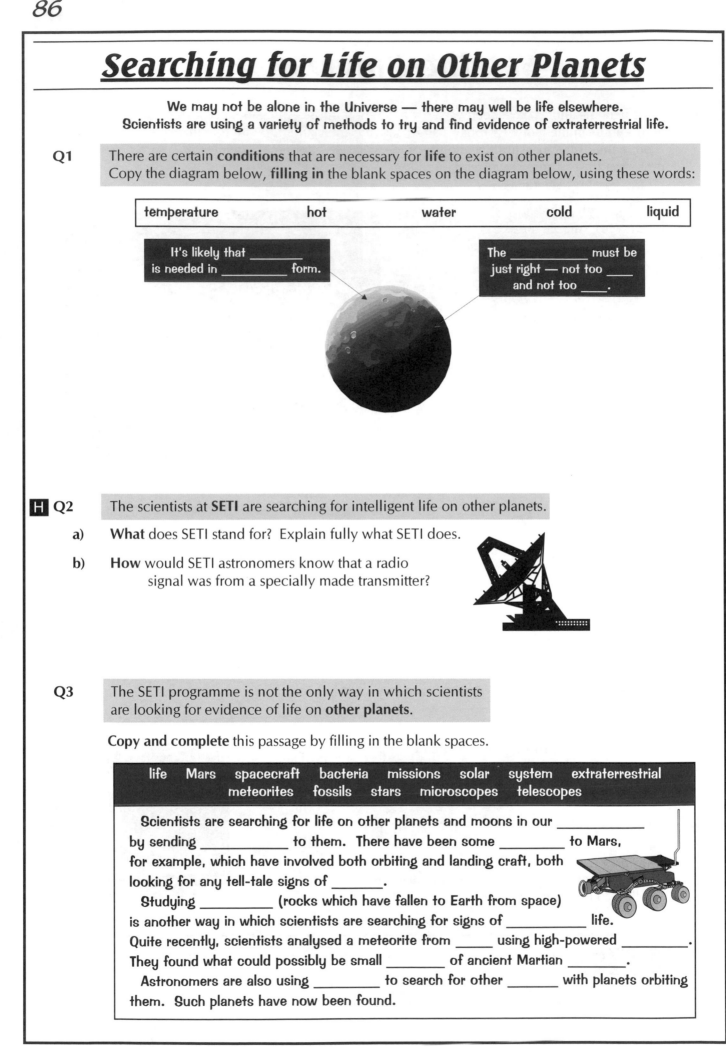

H Q2   The scientists at **SETI** are searching for intelligent life on other planets.

a)   **What** does SETI stand for? Explain fully what SETI does.

b)   **How** would SETI astronomers know that a radio signal was from a specially made transmitter?

Q3   The SETI programme is not the only way in which scientists are looking for evidence of life on **other planets**.

Copy and complete this passage by filling in the blank spaces.

| life   Mars   spacecraft   bacteria   missions   solar   system   extraterrestrial |
| meteorites   fossils   stars   microscopes   telescopes |

   Scientists are searching for life on other planets and moons in our _____
by sending _____ to them. There have been some _____ to Mars,
for example, which have involved both orbiting and landing craft, both
looking for any tell-tale signs of _____.
   Studying _____ (rocks which have fallen to Earth from space)
is another way in which scientists are searching for signs of _____ life.
Quite recently, scientists analysed a meteorite from _____ using high-powered _____.
They found what could possibly be small _____ of ancient Martian _____.
   Astronomers are also using _____ to search for other _____ with planets orbiting
them. Such planets have now been found.

The Universe

Q1   All the stars and galaxies that we see around us in the Universe today started off in the distant past as huge clouds of gas and dust. These clouds collapsed to form what we see today.

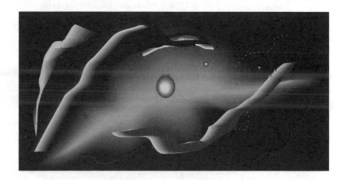

a) What caused the clouds to **collapse**?

b) As the clouds collapsed, nuclear fusion reactions began to occur within them. What caused these reactions to take place?

c) Explain what is believed to have happened when the nuclear reactions started.

The masses of some of the clouds were not large enough for nuclear reactions to begin when they collapsed.

d) Name **two** other things that may be formed when this occurs.

Q2   Our Solar System is part of the Milky Way.

a) What is the Milky Way?

b) At night-time, a milky white band can be seen stretching right across the sky. What characteristic of the Milky Way gives rise to this appearance?

Q3   Below are some facts about our Milky Way. For each one, decide whether it is **true** or **false**.

a) Neighbouring stars in the Milky Way are usually much further apart than the planets in the Solar System.

b) The Milky Way is at the centre of the Universe.

c) Our Solar System is at the centre of the Milky Way.

d) The Milky Way has spiral arms.

e) The stars we see at night are part of the Milky Way.

f) The Milky Way takes a long time to rotate.

g) The Milky Way is separated from its neighbours by lots of empty space.

h) There are still gas clouds in the Milky Way.

i) No more stars will form in the Milky Way.

The Life Cycle of Stars

Astronomers have been studying groups of stars. They have used their observations and mathematical models to come up with an idea for how they think some of the stars evolved.

This "Life Cycle" of a large star is illustrated in the diagram below.

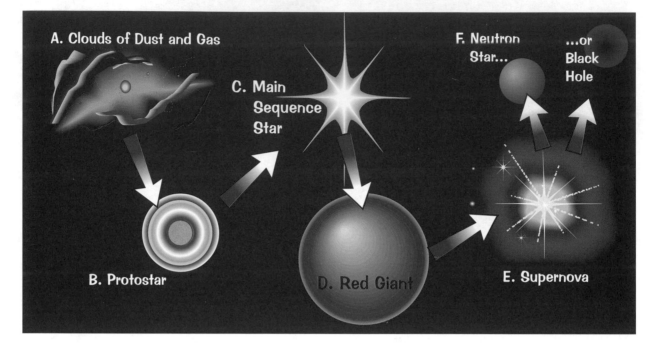

Q1 Which type of star is our Sun?

Q2 The scientists' ideas about stages A and B above are uncertain. Suggest why it is difficult to find **evidence** about these stages.

Q3 At a certain stage in the life cycle, the temperature inside a star exerts an outward force. What **causes** the inward opposing force?

Q4 At which stage in the cycle do these forces balance each other?

Q5 In the diagram above, many **heavier atoms** are made just before and during which stage?

Q6 What is happening to make the red giant star **redder** than a main sequence star?

Q7 How does the matter making up neutron stars **differ** from the matter we are used to on Earth?

Q8 **Explain why** astronomers need to study a group of stars rather than just one or two, when studying life cycles.

Q9 The first stars were almost completely formed from just two different elements. **Which elements are these**?

Q10 What is the process in which **energy** can be created when atoms are forced together?

Q11 Draw the life cycle for a small star (like our Sun).

The Origin of the Universe

H Q1 We know quite a lot about the Universe and how it is changing.

Name the **two main theories** that try to explain how the Universe began and continues to evolve.

You are here

H Q2 For each fact below, state which theory it could be explained by. (**Both** theories may apply)

a) The galaxies are all moving away from each other.

b) Galaxies have red shifts.

c) There seem to be galaxies in every direction.

d) Space is filled with a microwave background radiation coming from all directions.

e) Further away galaxies are moving away from us faster.

H Q3 When an object moves relative to an observer, the frequency of the electromagnetic radiation received by the observer changes.

a) What is the **name** of this effect?

b) What happens to the observed frequency if an object is **approaching**?

c) What happens to the observed frequency of an object that is **receding**?

d) **Give two examples** from everyday life of this effect in action.

Q4 A lot of the observations of the Universe can be explained by the **Steady State Theory**, but scientists have two big problems with it.

a) What is observed that cannot easily be explained by the theory?

b) What is the **other problem** that scientists point out with the theory?

The Future of the Universe

Q1   Two factors help to determine how the Universe evolves.

  a)   What are these two factors?

  b)   One of them is **easy** to measure, one is a **lot more difficult**. Which is which?

Q2   Measuring the total amount of mass in the Universe is not easy. Some matter is easy to see because it shines, and scientists can measure its mass. The rest is difficult, because we just cannot see it. For each of the objects below, choose which are **visible** and which are **invisible**.

> *Supergiant Stars*   *Interstellar Dust*   *White Dwarf Stars*
>
> *Black Holes*   *Black Dwarfs*
>
> *Main Sequence Stars*   *Dust between the Galaxies*

Q3   The Universe is expanding. We can be sure about this much.

  a)   What is the **name of the force** that could be slowing down the rate of expansion?

  b)   **What causes** this force?

  c)   If there were no forces acting, how would the Universe continue to evolve?

Q4   Scientists love drawing graphs to show what is happening in the Universe.
The graph below shows what has happened to the size of the Universe up to now.

  a)   The curve on the graph opposite is not a straight line but rises less and less steeply. What does this tell us about the expansion of the Universe?

  b)   On two copies of this graph, sketch the two possible futures for how the Universe might evolve from now on.

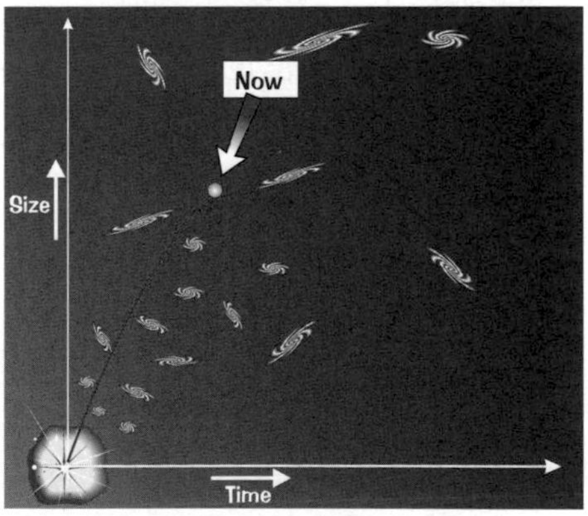

Q5   The end of the world as we know it....

  a)   What is the "**Big Crunch**"?

  b)   **How long** (at least...) have we got before it occurs? (if it occurs...)

Q6   Make another copy of the graph in Question 4. This time, extend it so that it illustrates a **cyclical Universe** — one that expands, then contracts, and then expands again.

Top Tips
That's it, then — the end of another section. And a pretty chunky section at that — covering everything from waves to outer space. Learn all this and you'll have a brain the size of a planet.

Speed, Velocity and Acceleration

Q1 Getting going! How fast is:

a) an athlete who runs 100m (metres) in 10s (seconds)?

b) a racing car zooming 240m in 12s?

c) a student, walking 600m in 240s?

d) a tortoise with a twisted ankle, shuffling 10m in 100s?

Q2 a) In the equation $\mathbf{a} = \dfrac{\Delta V}{\Delta t}$ state what a, ΔV and Δt stand for.

b) State the usual units of a, ΔV and Δt.

c) Explain how acceleration is different from speed and velocity.

Q3 This question is about a distance/time graph describing the motion of a car.

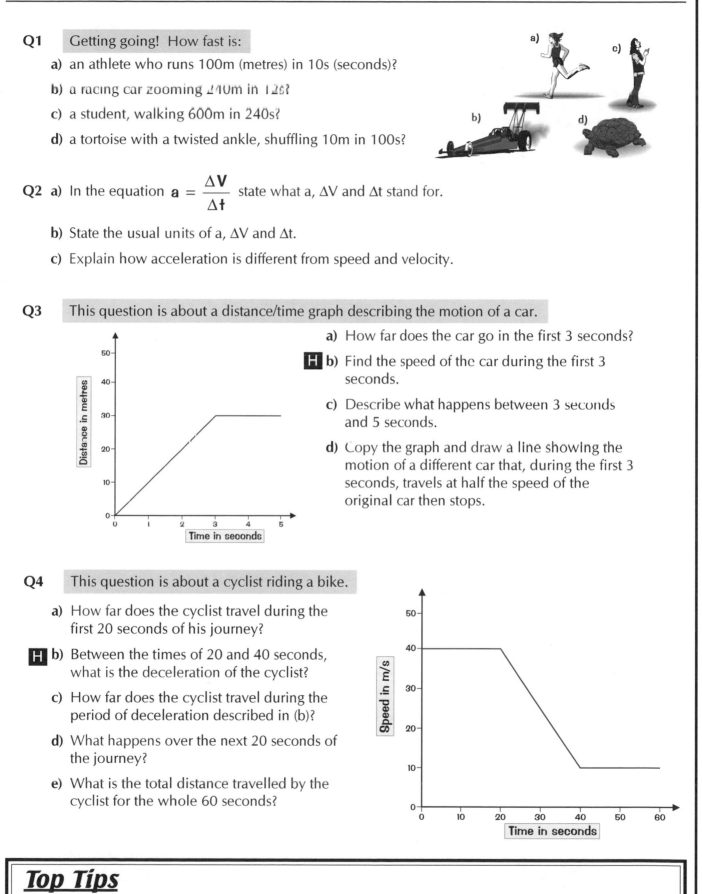

a) How far does the car go in the first 3 seconds?

H b) Find the speed of the car during the first 3 seconds.

c) Describe what happens between 3 seconds and 5 seconds.

d) Copy the graph and draw a line showing the motion of a different car that, during the first 3 seconds, travels at half the speed of the original car then stops.

Q4 This question is about a cyclist riding a bike.

a) How far does the cyclist travel during the first 20 seconds of his journey?

H b) Between the times of 20 and 40 seconds, what is the deceleration of the cyclist?

c) How far does the cyclist travel during the period of deceleration described in (b)?

d) What happens over the next 20 seconds of the journey?

e) What is the total distance travelled by the cyclist for the whole 60 seconds?

Top Tips

These graphs <u>look</u> similar, and it would be tempting to try and avoid learning all the differences between them. Be warned, if you don't know what all the details mean and you can't <u>distinguish</u> between the two types of graph, then you will get all these questions <u>wrong</u>. Harsh but true.

Forces and Motion

Q1 Newton's First Law of Motion states that balanced forces mean no change in velocity.

Explain clearly the highlighted terms (balanced forces and velocity).

Q2 A car is moving forward with a steady horizontal velocity.

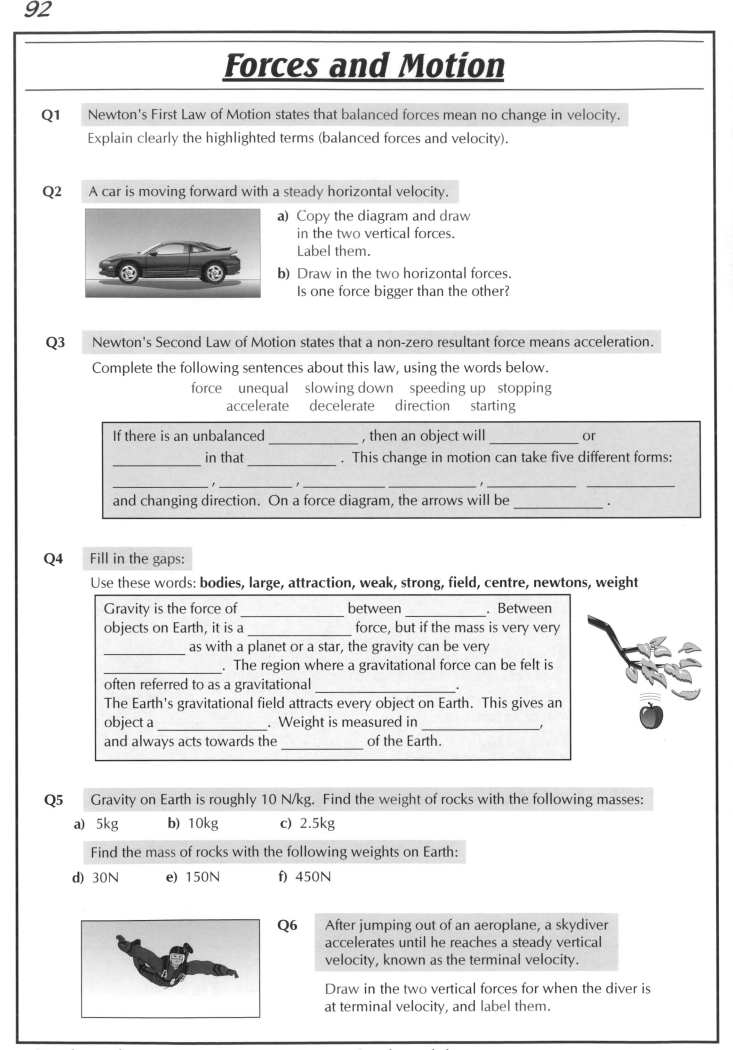

a) Copy the diagram and draw in the two vertical forces. Label them.

b) Draw in the two horizontal forces. Is one force bigger than the other?

Q3 Newton's Second Law of Motion states that a non-zero resultant force means acceleration.

Complete the following sentences about this law, using the words below.

force   unequal   slowing down   speeding up   stopping
accelerate   decelerate   direction   starting

> If there is an unbalanced _____ , then an object will _____ or
> _____ in that _____ . This change in motion can take five different forms:
> _____ , _____ , _____ _____ , _____ _____
> and changing direction. On a force diagram, the arrows will be _____ .

Q4 Fill in the gaps:

Use these words: **bodies, large, attraction, weak, strong, field, centre, newtons, weight**

> Gravity is the force of _____ between _____ . Between
> objects on Earth, it is a _____ force, but if the mass is very very
> _____ as with a planet or a star, the gravity can be very
> _____ . The region where a gravitational force can be felt is
> often referred to as a gravitational _____ .
> The Earth's gravitational field attracts every object on Earth. This gives an
> object a _____ . Weight is measured in _____ ,
> and always acts towards the _____ of the Earth.

Q5 Gravity on Earth is roughly 10 N/kg. Find the weight of rocks with the following masses:

a) 5kg   b) 10kg   c) 2.5kg

Find the mass of rocks with the following weights on Earth:

d) 30N   e) 150N   f) 450N

Q6 After jumping out of an aeroplane, a skydiver accelerates until he reaches a steady vertical velocity, known as the terminal velocity.

Draw in the two vertical forces for when the diver is at terminal velocity, and label them.

Energy Transfer & Energy Conservation

Q1 What is the significant type of energy involved in each of the following?

a) A drawn longbow.

b) A welder's red hot rivet.

c) A mole of unstable uranium-235 atoms.

d) A piece of glowing magnesium.

e) A plate balancing on a pole.

f) A wire carrying a telephone conversation.

g) A high-calorie birthday cake.

h) A speeding bullet.

Q2 In each of the following examples, energy is being changed from one type into another. In some cases, two or more types may be produced. State what the changes are for:

a) a descending rollercoaster car,

b) a crossbow bolt hitting a target,

c) a singer shouting into a microphone,

d) a cycle wheel spinning a dynamo,

e) a yo-yo climbing up its string,

f) a match being struck,

g) a magnifying glass concentrating the Sun's rays to burn a hole in a piece of paper,

h) a battery driving an analogue clock (one with hands),

i) a diver coming down on a springboard.

Q3 Copy and complete the following sentences which summarise the Principle of the Conservation of Energy:

Energy can never be _____ or _____ .
It is only ever _____ from one form to another.

Q4 Look at the energy flow diagram shown here. For each of the examples given below, draw an energy flow diagram. The first one has been done for you.

ENERGY INPUT → USEFUL DEVICE → USEFUL ENERGY OUTPUT
WASTED ENERGY
HEAT AND SOUND

a) electric hoist

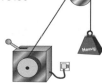

Electric energy → HOIST → potential energy of load
↓
wasted sound and heat

b) electric light bulb

c) electric motor

d) petrol-driven car

Efficiency

Q1 A student wants to find out about the efficiency of a stereo system rated at 20 watts sound output. She buys some batteries, which store 400,000 joules of chemical energy. When the new batteries are put into the stereo, and the machine is switched on to play a tape, the batteries are exhausted after 5 hours.

a) How much energy has the stereo usefully given out?

b) What is the efficiency of the tape recorder?

c) How would energy have been wasted?

d) If the stereo is used on the radio setting, would you expect the batteries to last longer? Explain your answer.

Q2 A handyman is using an electric sander with a rechargeable battery. He charges up the sander with 2500 joules of electrical energy. It should require 20 joules of energy to sand each m² of surface. At the end of three hours, the rechargeable battery is exhausted. He checks his work, and finds that he has actually covered an area of 100m².

a) How much useful energy has gone into the sanding?

b) What is the efficiency of the machine?

Q3 In today's motor vehicles, lots of valuable chemical energy is changed to types of energy that are of no use to us at all.

a) What are these useless types of energy?

b) Where in the vehicle might this energy be wasted (there may be more than one place)?

Q4 Some people might say that wind power and hydroelectric power are examples of getting energy for nothing. Are they correct, and if not, where is the energy coming from?

Q5 As you know, no energy transfer device is ever 100% efficient. This is because we cannot prevent the device from transferring the input energy into other, unwanted forms of energy. What are the two most common forms of unwanted energy produced by everyday appliances?

Q6 An electric heater might be 100% efficient — the exception to the rule!

a) Explain why it can be considered to be 100% efficient.

b) Is any energy wasted before it reaches the heater, and if so where?

Top Tips

Energy efficiency — it's not just washing machines and light bulbs. But it is pretty simple — just one thing over another. If it comes out to more than **100%** then you've probably got it **upside down**. If not, it's probably right. All very simple, so just hope it comes up in your Exam, and **easy marks** will be yours.

Heat Transfer and Conduction

Q1 The paragraph that follows is all about heat conduction. You have to use the following words to fill in the gaps. The words may be used once, more than once or not at all:

neighbouring collide carry reflect electrons pockets vibrate
close good poor solids

Conduction is the main form of heat transfer in _____. This is

because the particles are relatively _____. Extra heat energy

makes the particles _____ more. They pass on the extra

vibrational energy to _____ particles. Metals are

_____ conductors of heat energy because they contain many free

_____ which can move through the solid and _____ the

energy. The electrons give up their energy when they _____ with

other particles.

Q2 This diagram shows a metal bar with a number of holes drilled into it. The holes are just big enough to fit thermometers in. Four thermometers are put into the holes, and initially read the same temperature. The bar is then heated at one end with a Bunsen burner.

a) Redraw the diagram showing the levels recorded by the thermometers after a few minutes.

b) Explain the levels you have drawn.

c) Redraw the diagram showing the results if the same experiment was carried out using a bar of the same dimensions made from a poorer conductor.

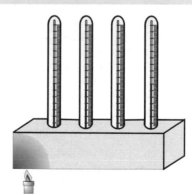

Q3 Sharon and Esme have booked a winter holiday in a log cabin. Sharon thinks that wood is a good substance to keep the holiday dwellers warm.

a) Do you agree?

They have a relaxing evening playing cards while it is cold and stormy outside. Esme goes up to the door. The body of the door is warm to the touch, but when she touches the brass handle, it feels very cold.

b) Explain why this is.

Convection and Radiation

Q1   Below are a number of descriptions of heat transfer processes. State whether they are concerned with conduction, convection, radiation or all three.

> **a)**   Heat flowing between two places when there is a difference in temperature.
>
> **b)**   Heat passing from atom to atom (most effective in solid materials).
>
> **c)**   Can occur through transparent substances.
>
> **d)**   Sets up movement currents in liquids and gases.
>
> **e)**   Is affected by colour and shininess.
>
> **f)**   Can occur through a vacuum.
>
> **g)**   Involves hot fluid expanding and rising.

Q2   It's a hot day at the beach, and the only shelter from the Sun is behind an advertising hoarding. It is cooler where you are sitting, with your back against the hoarding, but your friend is still sweltering next to you. From your side, the board all looks the same colour.

a)   What could be causing the difference?

b)   You look out at the beach, which is pretty deserted as it's so hot. You see a sunbed covered in white cloth with black plastic arms. There is a heat haze over the arms, but none over the cloth. Explain why.

Q3   An author is planning to write an adventure novel.

a)   The hero of the novel has to survive in the desert Sun having been tied up, in a car, by evil villains. Is he more likely to survive in a light coloured one or a dark coloured one?

b)   Evening brings a new torture. The desert nights can be very cold. Which car will now be the most comfortable?

Q4   The diagram below shows water being heated in an electric kettle. The arrows represent convection currents in the water. Complete the following passage by circling the correct words.

> Water next to the heating element is warmed and so [expands / contracts].
> This means its density [increases / decreases] and so it [rises / falls].
> Once away from the heating element, the water temperature
> [increases / decreases]. This results in it [contracting / expanding],
> which leads to a [lower / higher] density and so it [rises / falls]. This cooler
> water is then heated by the element again and the convection current continues.

Top Tips

The main thing is the <u>three methods</u> of <u>heat transfer</u>. Get that sorted and you'll be ready for anything in the Exams. You need to be able to say what's <u>happening</u> in each type of transfer, and <u>recognise</u> the <u>situations</u> where they to occur. Don't forget, <u>more than one</u> type of heat transfer can happen at the same time.

Heat Transfer and Insulation

Q1 Write down three insulating substances and three conducting substances, then complete a table like this.

Name of Substance	Conductor or Insulator	Used for

Q2 Explain the following, using ideas of heat transfer.

a) Frosty nights in winter are usually clear.

b) In a hot water tank, the heater is generally at the bottom, and the outlet is usually at the top.

H c) A layer of snow can stop young plants dying in the frost.

d) A shiny teapot keeps tea hot longer than a dull one.

H e) Birds try to keep warm in winter by ruffling up their feathers.

f) Holding the legs of a transistor with pliers when it is being soldered can prevent heat damage to the transistor.

Q3 The vacuum flask has a number of features which help it to insulate its contents.

Some features are listed below. For each of them, say which method of heat transfer they are reducing, and how they do this.

a) The cap is covered in plastic.

b) The cap is filled with cork.

c) The liquid is contained in a glass bottle.

d) There is a vacuum between the two walls of the glass bottle.

e) The outside of the inner glass layer is silvered.

f) The inside of the outer glass layer is silvered.

g) The bottle is surrounded by air inside the plastic case.

h) The bottle is supported away from the casing by insulating foam.

Outer cap/cup

Plastic cap filled with cork

Shiny mirrored surfaces

Vacuum

Sponge

Hot or cold liquid

Air

Plastic case

Keeping Buildings Warm

Q1 Below is a list of methods of saving energy.

Describe how each saves heat energy, and give the type of heat transfer that the insulation method affects.

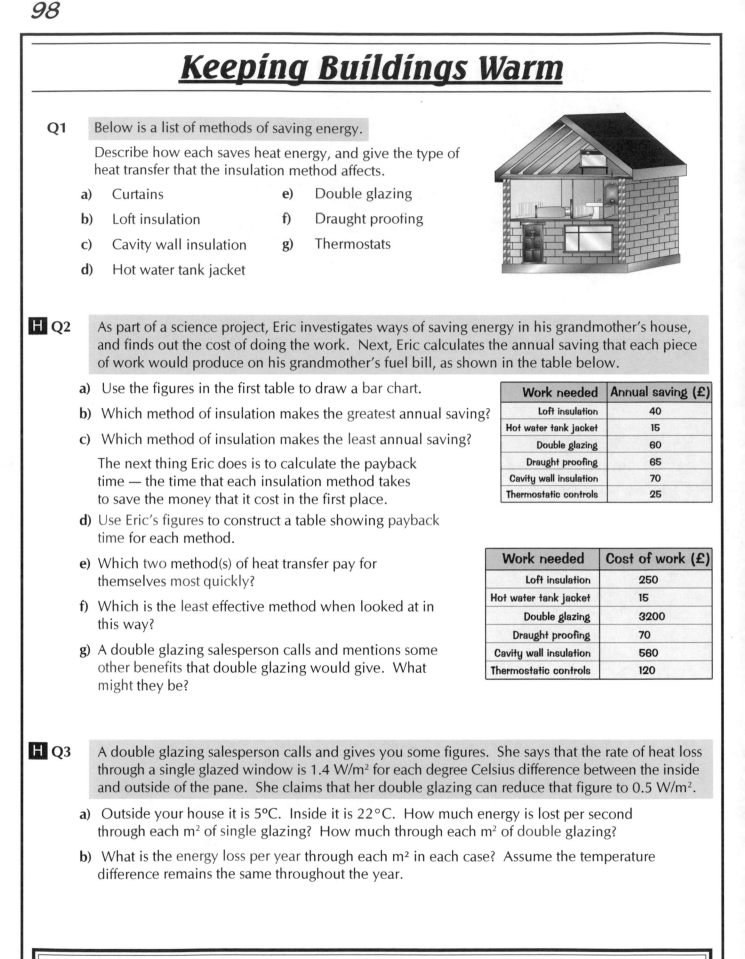

a) Curtains

b) Loft insulation

c) Cavity wall insulation

d) Hot water tank jacket

e) Double glazing

f) Draught proofing

g) Thermostats

H Q2 As part of a science project, Eric investigates ways of saving energy in his grandmother's house, and finds out the cost of doing the work. Next, Eric calculates the annual saving that each piece of work would produce on his grandmother's fuel bill, as shown in the table below.

a) Use the figures in the first table to draw a bar chart.

b) Which method of insulation makes the greatest annual saving?

c) Which method of insulation makes the least annual saving?

The next thing Eric does is to calculate the payback time — the time that each insulation method takes to save the money that it cost in the first place.

d) Use Eric's figures to construct a table showing payback time for each method.

e) Which two method(s) of heat transfer pay for themselves most quickly?

f) Which is the least effective method when looked at in this way?

g) A double glazing salesperson calls and mentions some other benefits that double glazing would give. What might they be?

Work needed	Annual saving (£)
Loft insulation	40
Hot water tank jacket	15
Double glazing	60
Draught proofing	65
Cavity wall insulation	70
Thermostatic controls	25

Work needed	Cost of work (£)
Loft insulation	250
Hot water tank jacket	15
Double glazing	3200
Draught proofing	70
Cavity wall insulation	560
Thermostatic controls	120

H Q3 A double glazing salesperson calls and gives you some figures. She says that the rate of heat loss through a single glazed window is 1.4 W/m² for each degree Celsius difference between the inside and outside of the pane. She claims that her double glazing can reduce that figure to 0.5 W/m².

a) Outside your house it is 5°C. Inside it is 22°C. How much energy is lost per second through each m² of single glazing? How much through each m² of double glazing?

b) What is the energy loss per year through each m² in each case? Assume the temperature difference remains the same throughout the year.

Top Tips

Examiners like asking you about these sorts of things — so make sure you <u>know</u> the <u>functions</u> of all the <u>parts of the vacuum flask</u>, and how all of the <u>insulation methods</u> work. Having an idea of the <u>cost</u> of each insulation method will help — and you need to know how "<u>payback time</u>" is calculated and used.

Section Nine — Forces, Energy and Radioactivity

Energy Resources

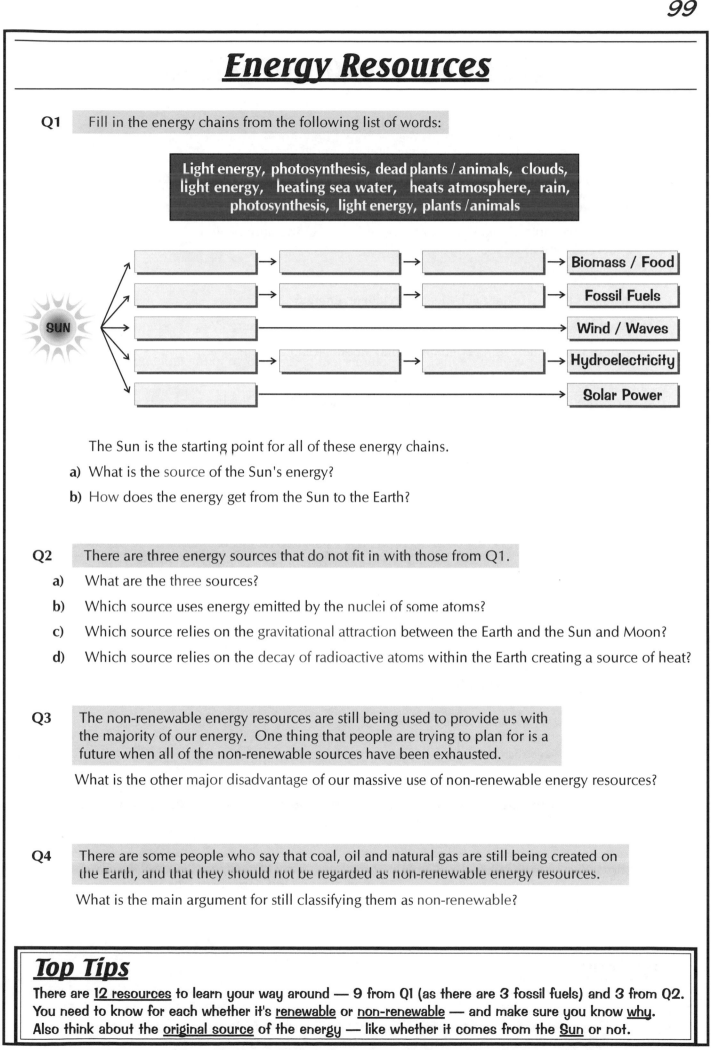

Q1 Fill in the energy chains from the following list of words:

> Light energy, photosynthesis, dead plants / animals, clouds,
> light energy, heating sea water, heats atmosphere, rain,
> photosynthesis, light energy, plants /animals

The Sun is the starting point for all of these energy chains.

a) What is the source of the Sun's energy?

b) How does the energy get from the Sun to the Earth?

Q2 There are three energy sources that do not fit in with those from Q1.

a) What are the three sources?

b) Which source uses energy emitted by the nuclei of some atoms?

c) Which source relies on the gravitational attraction between the Earth and the Sun and Moon?

d) Which source relies on the decay of radioactive atoms within the Earth creating a source of heat?

Q3 The non-renewable energy resources are still being used to provide us with the majority of our energy. One thing that people are trying to plan for is a future when all of the non-renewable sources have been exhausted.

What is the other major disadvantage of our massive use of non-renewable energy resources?

Q4 There are some people who say that coal, oil and natural gas are still being created on the Earth, and that they should not be regarded as non-renewable energy resources.

What is the main argument for still classifying them as non-renewable?

Top Tips

There are <u>12 resources</u> to learn your way around — 9 from Q1 (as there are 3 fossil fuels) and 3 from Q2.
You need to know for each whether it's <u>renewable</u> or <u>non-renewable</u> — and make sure you know <u>why</u>.
Also think about the <u>original source</u> of the energy — like whether it comes from the <u>Sun</u> or not.

Power Stations Using Non-Renewables

Q1   Despite scientific research into alternative sources of energy, most of the electricity that we use today is generated from 4 non-renewable energy sources.

a)   Give the names of these 4 sources.

b)   A traditional power station relies on the combustion of 3 of these sources. Which are the three that are burned?

c)   Draw one simple block diagram to show the general structure of all 3 types of traditional power station.

d)   Where will the chemical energy be changed into heat energy?

e)   Where is the heat energy changed into kinetic energy?

f)   What happens to produce the kinetic energy from the heat energy?

g)   Where is the kinetic energy changed into kinetic (rotational) energy?

g)   Where is energy converted into electrical form?

h)   How does the electrical energy get from the power station to the users?

i)   Draw an energy chain showing how the energy types change.

Q2   All of the non-renewable energy sources have associated environmental problems. On a copy of this table, put ticks to indicate which problems are associated with each source.

Problem	Coal	Oil	Gas	Nuclear
Release of CO_2 contributing to Greenhouse Effect				
Acid rain production				
Devastation of landscape				
Environmental problems due to spillage at sea				
Expensive plant and clean-up after use				
Production of dangerous, long-lasting waste				
Danger of major catastrophe				

Q3   Fossil fuels took millions of years to be formed. They are vital chemical raw materials and we just send them up in smoke. Our man-made world depends on fossil fuels.

Give two examples of materials we would lose if fossil fuels ran out and suggest what alternatives we could use.

Top Tips

It's a good idea to be well up on the _environmental problems_ associated with each of the forms of power production, as examiners are very keen on these. Learn the _energy changes_ taking place at the different stages, not forgetting where energy is _lost_ — and think about how fuel stocks can be _conserved_.

Wind Power and Hydroelectric Power

Q1 Copy and complete the following paragraph about extracting power from the wind, using the following.

> increase   remote   high   zero   5000   windmills   coasts
> large   wind turbines   noise   moors   blades
> generator   view

The energy of the wind can be extracted using devices called _____, or more properly _____ _____. These can be situated in _____ areas, such as _____ and _____ where there is a reliable history of wind. Each wind turbine contains its own _____. The wind turns the _____, providing the rotational energy needed to generate the electricity. Once the wind turbine is operating there is little material pollution, but people can complain about the _____ and the spoiling of the _____. In order to replace one coal-fired power station it would require about _____ turbines, and this would cover a _____ area of ground. Problems involved with wind generated electricity include _____ initial costs, _____ power being generated when the wind stops, and not having any way to _____ supply when there is extra demand.

Q2 This diagram shows a pumped storage reservoir system. The labels have been replaced with letters.

Match up the letters with the labels.

turbines ☐

upper reservoir ☐

generator ☐

pump ☐

lower reservoir ☐

direction at night ☐

national grid ☐

direction during peak demand ☐

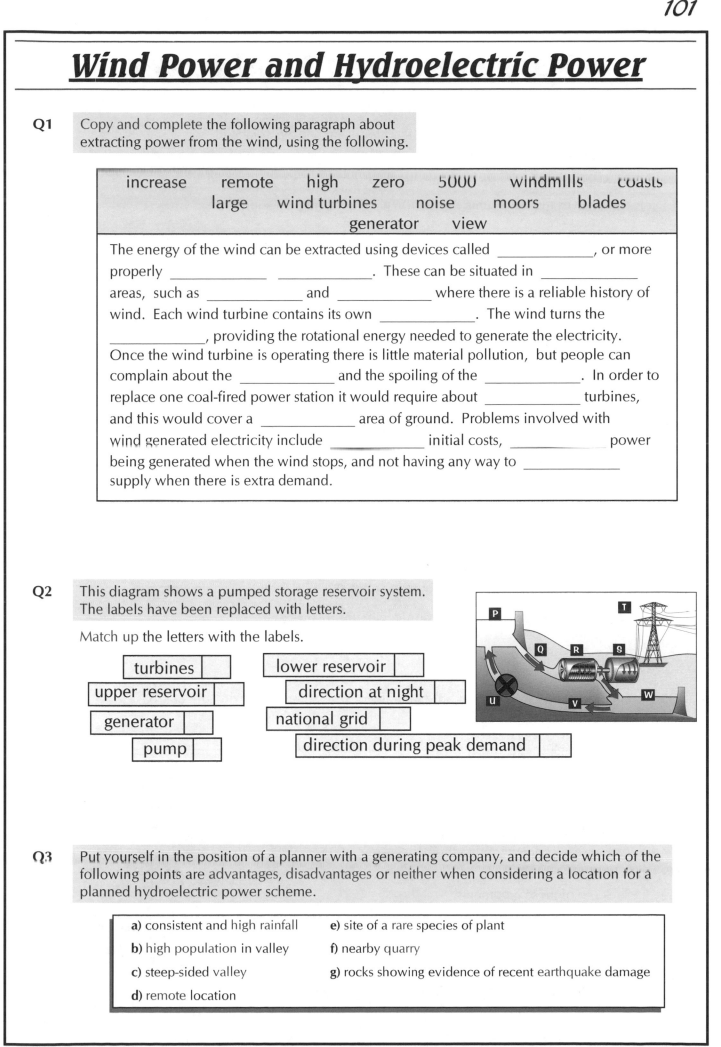

Q3 Put yourself in the position of a planner with a generating company, and decide which of the following points are advantages, disadvantages or neither when considering a location for a planned hydroelectric power scheme.

a) consistent and high rainfall   e) site of a rare species of plant

b) high population in valley   f) nearby quarry

c) steep-sided valley   g) rocks showing evidence of recent earthquake damage

d) remote location

Wave Power and Tidal Power

Q1   The most recent design of wave generator uses the energy in
water waves to drive a turbine and therefore generate electricity.

   a)   As waves travel towards the shore, what is the main direction of vibration of the water molecules?

   b)   How is this motion used to generate electricity?

   c)   What gives the waves this energy? What was its original source?

Q2   Once the wave generators are in place, there is little or no pollution of a chemical nature.
However, as with any large-scale development, some people will be affected.

   Give an example of one such group of people and say how they're likely to be affected.

Q3   In practice, the heights of tides vary throughout the month according to the relative
positions of the Sun and Moon. 'Spring' tides are when the variation between high
and low tides is the greatest, while 'neap' tides have the smallest variation.

   What implications does this monthly cycle have for tidal power schemes?

Q4   Some people have said that about 100 tidal power stations, situated all around
the coast of Britain, could generate the entire electricity needs of the country.

   What particular drawbacks can you see with this plan?

Q5   Tidal power stations are not only suitable for generating power on a regular basis,
but they can also be used to store energy for periods of high demand.

   Indicate roughly how you think that this could be done.

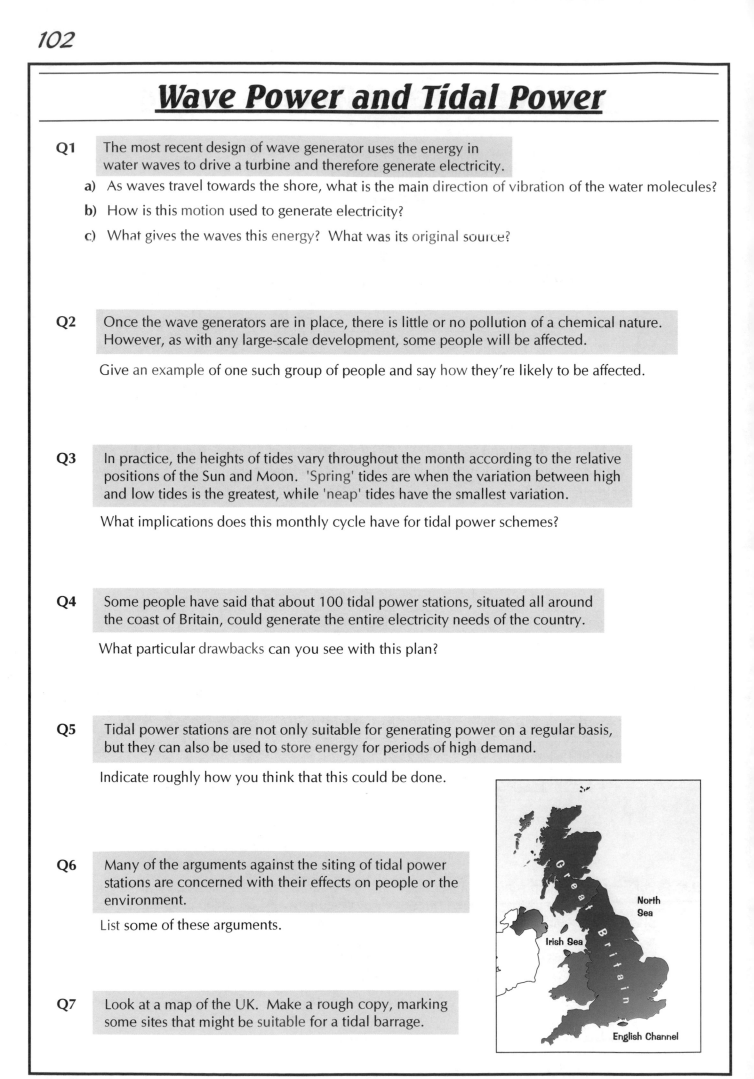

Q6   Many of the arguments against the siting of tidal power
stations are concerned with their effects on people or the
environment.

   List some of these arguments.

Q7   Look at a map of the UK. Make a rough copy, marking
some sites that might be suitable for a tidal barrage.

Section Nine — Forces, Energy and Radioactivity

Geothermal and Wood Burning

Q1 One of the places in the world where geothermal energy is being used to contribute to the overall energy needs is Reykjavik in Iceland.

Greenland Sea

Iceland

Reykjavik

Atlantic Ocean

In the city of Reykjavik, water can be pumped up from underground at varying temperatures between 95°C and 135°C. This can be used for direct heating of the houses. Early Norse settlers did exactly the same thing in Iceland when they first settled there.

When the temperature of 1kg of water drops by 1°C, 4200 joules of heat energy are lost to the surroundings. In the 1970s, 16 boreholes supplied Reykjavik with 8000kg of water every minute.

a) If the water entered the system at 130°C, and left at a temperature of 30°C, calculate how much energy this represents over a 24 hour period.

b) How much power would be generated if all of this energy could be converted directly into electrical energy?

c) What could the water leaving the system at 30°C be used for?

Q2 Why do geothermal sources have such a long life?

Q3 **Put** the stages in the generation of electricity from wood burning in their correct order.

> harvest trees,   burn in power station furnace,   cultivate fast-growing trees,
> produce steam,   chop up trees,   generate electricity,   power turbine

Q4 An environmental group has started up a campaign against plans to run a trial with a wood burning power scheme. They claim that the main product of burning the wood will be carbon dioxide, which will add significantly to the Greenhouse Effect.

Is this a valid argument? Explain.

Q5 A shady local businessman claims that he can get hold of wood much cheaper from the rainforests in a developing country. He says that as you need wood, it doesn't matter where it comes from, and the developing country will be grateful for the money.

What are the ecological arguments against taking him up on his offer?

Q6 What could you do to try and convince those who say that huge forests of identical trees would be a real eyesore, and use up too much of the land?

Q7 The burning of wood in the furnace would still lead to some of the problems associated with burning coal in more traditional power stations. What do you think they could be?

Section Nine — Forces, Energy and Radioactivity

Solar Energy

Q1 a) What are the three different ways of harnessing solar energy shown below?

b) Here are a number of statements about solar energy.
Decide which of the three methods they apply to:

    i) The Sun's rays are focused onto one spot.

    ii) Electric currents are produced directly.

    iii) Curved mirrors reflect rays from the Sun.

    iv) A matt black surface absorbs solar radiation.

    v) Water is turned into steam to drive a turbine.

    vi) Initial costs are very high relative to output.

    vii) Water pipes feed in cold water and take away warmer water.

    viii) Extremely high temperatures are produced.

Q2 An architect is designing a house that will rely on solar panels to heat some of the water for the central heating. He wants to use a silver material for the panels, as this will look futuristic.

Explain why this is not a good colour for the panels, and tell him where exactly the panels should be placed.

Q3 A local newspaper has started a campaign to get a solar furnace built in the UK.

List three disadvantages there would be to locating such a power generator here.

Q4 A solar cell array is to be fitted to a satellite that is going to be launched into an orbit around the Earth. It's reckoned that the total solar power arriving in the region of the Earth is 1350 W/m². A new design of solar cell is 10% efficient. When the satellite is functioning fully, its power consumption will be 3.3kW.

a) Calculate the area of solar cells needed.

b) Will there be restrictions on when the satellite is able to be fully operational?

c) For a solar powered machine to operate at the Earth's surface, how would the area of cell array compare? Explain.

Top Tips
There are <u>three</u> methods of <u>directly</u> using the <u>Sun's energy</u> here — so in your Exam you must be sure which one you're talking about. Learn how each one works, and what the <u>disadvantages</u> are.
Think about our <u>weather</u>, and what use each of the methods would be in Britain.

Section Nine — Forces, Energy and Radioactivity

Atoms and Radioactivity

Q1 The diagram below shows the apparatus used by Lord Rutherford to probe the structure of the atom.

a) Name the particles that are directed at the gold foil.

b) Why does this apparatus need to operate in a vacuum?

c) Which of the detectors measures the highest count rate?

d) Some particles are detected at Y. Explain this observation using your knowledge of atomic structure.

e) Just a very small fraction of the incident particles are scattered more than 90° by the foil (some of these are detected by detector Z).
What does this tell you about the nuclei of the gold atoms?

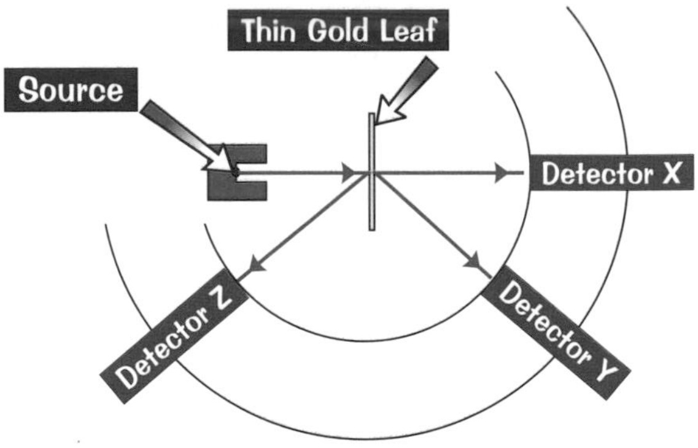

f) Gold was chosen as the target for this experiment. Give a reason for this choice.

g) Explain why a gaseous target would be unsuitable.

Q2 The following paragraph is about the background nuclear radiation on Earth. Fill in the blank spaces using the given words.

exposed	cosmic rays	rocks	background	natural	soil	radioactive	outer space

Throughout our daily lives we are all _____ to nuclear radiation from _____ sources. This is commonly called _____ radiation. Some of this radiation comes from the _____ and _____ around us. This is because they both contain small amounts of _____ substances. Another source of background radiation is _____ .
Radiation called _____ bombards the Earth and adds to the natural radiation levels.

Q3 Is the decay of an unstable nucleus affected by physical conditions such as temperature and chemical bonding?

Q4 The decay of a nucleus is said to be a random process. Explain what this means.

The Three Types of Radiation

Q1 Some physical properties of alpha, beta and gamma radiation are shown to the right.

Match each to the correct radiation.

| Alpha | Beta | Gamma |

| Electromagnetic Waves | | Zero mass |

| Electrons | Very short wavelength | Helium nucleus |

| γ | | α |

| Charge = -1 | Mass no. = 4 | β |

Q2 The diagram below shows alpha, beta and gamma radiation being fired at a line of obstacles.

a) Copy the diagram.
For each particle, draw a line to show the path it travels before it is absorbed.

b) Give a reason why alpha particles only penetrate a short distance into a material.

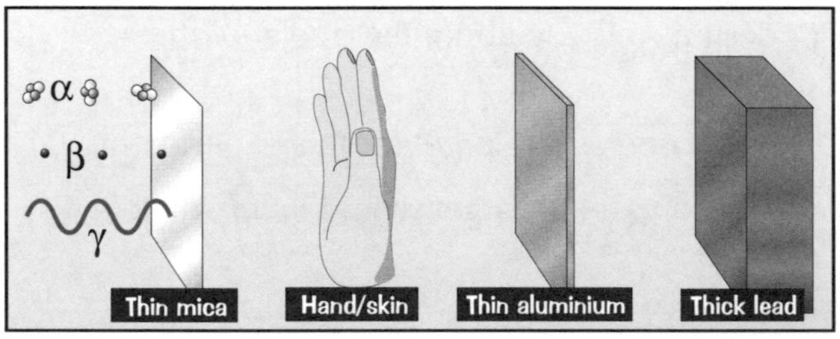

Thin mica　　Hand/skin　　Thin aluminium　　Thick lead

Q3 For each question **a)** to **g)**, state which of alpha particles, beta particles and gamma radiation:

a) has the largest mass?

b) travels at the speed of light?

c) causes the most ionisation?

d) has zero electrical charge?

e) is present in background radiation?

f) is identical to a helium nucleus?

g) is an electron travelling at high speed?

Q4 Copy and complete the following sentences about the half-life of radioactive atoms.

| zero | long | time | half | atoms | radioactivity | gamma |
| alpha | beta | short | nucleus | decreases | decay |

The _____ of a sample always _____ over time. Each time a decay happens _____, _____ or _____ radiation is emitted. This means a radioactive _____ has decayed.
The problem with trying to measure the time for all the atoms to decay is that the activity never reaches _____.
The half-life is the _____ taken for _____ of the radioactive _____ now present to _____. An isotope with a _____ half-life decays more quickly than an isotope with a _____ half-life.

Using and Detecting Radiation

Q1 This question concerns the treatment of cancer using radiotherapy.

    a) High doses of gamma rays can be used to treat cancers. What effect do gamma rays have on living cells?

    b) Explain why a patient on a course of radiotherapy feels very ill.

    c) For the treatment to be a success, list two factors that the radiotherapist needs to consider before starting the treatment?

Q2 Copy out the following paragraph and fill in the gaps.

> irradiation   dose   surgical   temperatures
> radioactive   sterilise   gamma   instruments   damage
> exposed   microbes   fresh   safe   emitter

> A high dose of _____ radiation can be used to _____ food, keeping it _____ for longer. The process kills harmful _____, but doesn't do much _____ to food, as it doesn't involve exposure to high _____ like boiling. The food is not _____ afterwards, so it is perfectly _____ to eat. The isotope needs to be a very strong _____ of gamma rays. This method can also be used to sterilise _____ _____ .

Q3 Look at the diagram below showing how the thickness of a metal sheet is kept constant by the use of a radiation source.

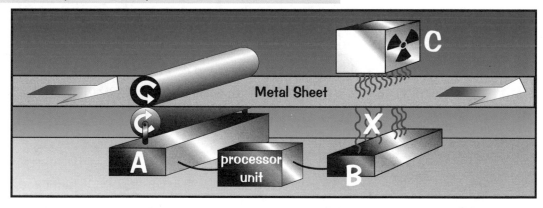

    a) Name A, B and C. What type of radiation is X?

    b) Suppose the thickness of the metal passing C increases. How does the system detect this change, and how does it return the thickness to its preset value?

    c) The radioactive isotope used here must have a long half-life. Explain what would go wrong if the half-life was only two hours.

    d) What type of radiation would you choose if you wanted to monitor the thickness of cardboard?

    e) Explain why gamma radiation would be the wrong choice of radiation in **d)**.

Q4 a) What equipment is used to detect radiation? How does it work?

    b) Radioactivity is measured in becquerels (Bq). What does a count of 60 Bq mean?

Q5 How is photographic film used to detect whether someone has been exposed to too much radioactivity?

Radiation Hazards and Safety

Q1   Radioactive particles can be harmful to living cells.

a) Which types of radiation can do this damage?

b) What process usually has to happen for damage to occur?

c) What do we call a cell that has been slightly altered, but not killed?

d) Why are these cells so dangerous?

e) What do we call the condition commonly caused by these cells?

Q2   Radioactive particles can also give a person "radiation sickness".

a) How could a person develop radiation sickness?

b) What happens to the body to cause radiation sickness?

Q3   List at least three factors which determine how much harm is done to a person when exposed to radiation.

Q4   Radiation outside the body —

What type(s) of radiation are most dangerous when outside the body? Explain your answer.

Q5   Radiation inside the body —

What type(s) of radiation are most dangerous when inside the body? Explain your answer.

Q6   There are rules to observe when handling radioactive materials in a school laboratory.

Fill in the gaps.

Never allow the source to come into contact with the _____.
_____ should always be used to handle radioactive materials.
Keep the source as _____ _____ the body as
possible. Point the source _____ _____ the
body. Avoid looking _____ at the source. Keep the source
in a box made from _____ . When the experiment is
finished, _____ the source as soon as possible.

Q7   People who work in the nuclear industry take even greater precautions.

Describe precautions workers can take to protect themselves from the following risks:

a) Tiny radioactive particles being inhaled or getting stuck on the skin.

b) Areas highly contaminated with gamma radiation.

c) Areas too dangerous even for the best-protected workers.

Top Tips

More great examples of radiation, which you **WILL** need, so add them to your **brain-file**. You already know that **radiation** can be **dangerous**, but you need to learn all the **safety precautions**. I realise they aren't all that **exciting**, but they can ask you to **list** them in the Exam for some nice easy marks.

Section Nine — Forces, Energy and Radioactivity